# Quality Function Deployment and Lean-Six Sigma
# Applications in Public Health

Also available from ASQ Quality Press:

*The Public Health Quality Improvement Handbook*
Ron Bialek, John W. Moran, and Grace L. Duffy

*Lean Doctors: A Bold and Practical Guide to Using Lean Principles to Transform Healthcare Systems, One Doctor at a Time*
Aneesh Suneja with Carolyn Suneja

*Root Cause Analysis and Improvement in the Healthcare Sector: A Step-by-Step Guide*
Bjørn Andersen, Tom Fagerhaug, and Marti Beltz

*Solutions to the Healthcare Quality Crisis: Cases and Examples of Lean Six Sigma in Healthcare*
Soren Bisgaard, editor

*On Becoming Exceptional: SSM Health Care's Journey to Baldrige and Beyond*
Sister Mary Jean Ryan, FSM

*Journey to Excellence: Baldrige Health Care Leaders Speak Out*
Kathleen Goonan, editor

*A Lean Guide to Transforming Healthcare: How to Implement Lean Principles in Hospitals, Medical Offices, Clinics, and Other Healthcare Organizations*
Thomas G. Zidel

*Benchmarking for Hospitals: Achieving Best-in-Class Performance without Having to Reinvent the Wheel*
Victor Sower, Jo Ann Duffy, and Gerald Kohers

*Lean-Six Sigma for Healthcare, Second Edition: A Senior Leader Guide to Improving Cost and Throughput*
Greg Butler, Chip Caldwell, and Nancy Poston

*Lean Six Sigma for the Healthcare Practice: A Pocket Guide*
Roderick A. Munro

*5S for Service Organizations and Offices: A Lean Look at Improvements*
Debashis Sarkar

To request a complimentary catalog of ASQ Quality Press publications, call 800-248-1946, or visit our Web site at http://www.asq.org/quality-press.

# Quality Function Deployment and Lean-Six Sigma Applications in Public Health

Grace L. Duffy

John W. Moran

William Riley

ASQ Quality Press
Milwaukee, Wisconsin

American Society for Quality, Quality Press, Milwaukee 53203
© 2010 American Society for Quality
All rights reserved. Published 2010
Printed in the United States of America
14 13 12 11 10    5 4 3 2 1

**Library of Congress Cataloging-in-Publication Data**
Duffy, Grace L.
  Quality function deployment and lean-six sigma applications in public health / Grace L. Duffy, John W. Moran, William Riley.
     p. cm.
  Includes bibliographical references and index.
  ISBN 978-0-87389-787-7 (casebound : alk. paper)
  1. Public health—Quality control.  2. Medical care—Quality control.  3. Six sigma (Quality control standard)  I. Moran, John W.  II. Riley, William.  III. Title.

  RA399.A3D84 2006
  362.1068—dc22
                              2010005632

ISBN-13: 978-0-87389-787-7

Publisher: William A. Tony
Acquisitions Editor: Matt Meinholz
Project Editor: Paul O'Mara
Production Administrator: Randall Benson

ASQ Mission: The American Society for Quality advances individual, organizational, and community excellence worldwide through learning, quality improvement, and knowledge exchange.

Attention Bookstores, Wholesalers, Schools, and Corporations: ASQ Quality Press books, videotapes, audiotapes, and software are available at quantity discounts with bulk purchases for business, educational, or instructional use. For information, please contact ASQ Quality Press at 800–248–1946, or write to ASQ Quality Press, P.O. Box 3005, Milwaukee, WI 53201-3005.

Quality Press
600 N. Plankinton Avenue
Milwaukee, Wisconsin 53203
Call toll free 800-248-1946
Fax 414-272-1734
www.asq.org
http://www.asq.org/quality-press
http://standardsgroup.asq.org
E-mail: authors@asq.org

To place orders or to request a free copy of the ASQ Quality Press Publications Catalog, including ASQ membership information, call 800-248-1946. Visit our Web site at www.asq.org or http://www.asq.org/quality-press.

 Printed on acid-free paper

# Contents

*Preface* . . . . . . . . . . . . . . . . . . . . . . . . . . . . . . . . . . . . . . . . . . . . . . . . . . . . . . . . . . . . . . . . . . . . . . . *xiii*

*Acknowledgments* . . . . . . . . . . . . . . . . . . . . . . . . . . . . . . . . . . . . . . . . . . . . . . . . . . . . . *xv*

**Chapter 1: The Continuum of Quality Improvement in Public Health** . . . . . . . . . . . . **1**

Introduction . . . . . . . . . . . . . . . . . . . . . . . . . . . . . . . . . . . . . . . . . . . . . . . . . . . . . . . . . . . . . 1
Process Improvement in a Public Health Department . . . . . . . . . . . . . . . . . . . . . . . . 3
Little "qi" . . . . . . . . . . . . . . . . . . . . . . . . . . . . . . . . . . . . . . . . . . . . . . . . . . . . . . . . . . . . . 3
Big "QI" . . . . . . . . . . . . . . . . . . . . . . . . . . . . . . . . . . . . . . . . . . . . . . . . . . . . . . . . . . . . . . 5
Large-Scale Public Health System Quality Improvement . . . . . . . . . . . . . . . . . . . . . . 6
Big "QI," Little "qi," and Individual "qi" . . . . . . . . . . . . . . . . . . . . . . . . . . . . . . . . . 13
Conclusion . . . . . . . . . . . . . . . . . . . . . . . . . . . . . . . . . . . . . . . . . . . . . . . . . . . . . . . . . . 15
Endnotes . . . . . . . . . . . . . . . . . . . . . . . . . . . . . . . . . . . . . . . . . . . . . . . . . . . . . . . . . . . . 17

**Chapter 2: Introduction to Quality Function Deployment and Lean-Six Sigma** . . . . . . **19**

Introduction to Quality Function Deployment . . . . . . . . . . . . . . . . . . . . . . . . . . . . . . 19
Introduction to Lean-Six Sigma . . . . . . . . . . . . . . . . . . . . . . . . . . . . . . . . . . . . . . . . . 22
Summary . . . . . . . . . . . . . . . . . . . . . . . . . . . . . . . . . . . . . . . . . . . . . . . . . . . . . . . . . . . . 25
Endnotes . . . . . . . . . . . . . . . . . . . . . . . . . . . . . . . . . . . . . . . . . . . . . . . . . . . . . . . . . . . . 26

**Chapter 3: An Integrated QI Approach:**
**QFD and LSS Support Macro, Meso, Micro** . . . . . . . . . . . . . . . . . . . . . . . **27**

Introduction . . . . . . . . . . . . . . . . . . . . . . . . . . . . . . . . . . . . . . . . . . . . . . . . . . . . . . . . . . 27
Integrated Processes Create a System . . . . . . . . . . . . . . . . . . . . . . . . . . . . . . . . . . . . . 29
The Human Interaction with Macro, Meso, and Micro Levels: Individual QI . . . . . . . 33
Endnotes . . . . . . . . . . . . . . . . . . . . . . . . . . . . . . . . . . . . . . . . . . . . . . . . . . . . . . . . . . . . 36

**Chapter 4: Customer Focus: Revitalizing Your Organization**
**to Become Customer Centric** . . . . . . . . . . . . . . . . . . . . . . . . . . . . . . . . . **37**

Summary . . . . . . . . . . . . . . . . . . . . . . . . . . . . . . . . . . . . . . . . . . . . . . . . . . . . . . . . . . . . 47
Endnotes . . . . . . . . . . . . . . . . . . . . . . . . . . . . . . . . . . . . . . . . . . . . . . . . . . . . . . . . . . . . 47

**Chapter 5: Process Analysis and Waste Reduction** . . . . . . . . . . . . . . . . . . . . . . . . . . . **49**

Introduction . . . . . . . . . . . . . . . . . . . . . . . . . . . . . . . . . . . . . . . . . . . . . . . . . . . . . . . . . . 49
1. Understanding How a Process Is Structured . . . . . . . . . . . . . . . . . . . . . . . . . . . . . . 50
2. How to Analyze a Process . . . . . . . . . . . . . . . . . . . . . . . . . . . . . . . . . . . . . . . . . . . . 50
*Creating a Process Map* . . . . . . . . . . . . . . . . . . . . . . . . . . . . . . . . . . . . . . . . . . . . . . *51*
3. Identifying Inefficiencies in a Process Map . . . . . . . . . . . . . . . . . . . . . . . . . . . . . . 54

Process Features . . . . . . . . . . . . . . . . . . . . . . . . . . . . . . . . . . . . . . . . . . . . . 54
Two Types of Process Maps . . . . . . . . . . . . . . . . . . . . . . . . . . . . . . . . . . . . 55
   *Opportunity Map* . . . . . . . . . . . . . . . . . . . . . . . . . . . . . . . . . . . . . . . . . 56
   *Value Stream Mapping Definitions* . . . . . . . . . . . . . . . . . . . . . . . . . 57
   *Visualizing Patient Flow* . . . . . . . . . . . . . . . . . . . . . . . . . . . . . . . . . . 57
   *Current State Value Map* . . . . . . . . . . . . . . . . . . . . . . . . . . . . . . . . . 59
   *Future State Value Map* . . . . . . . . . . . . . . . . . . . . . . . . . . . . . . . . . . 60
Spaghetti Diagram . . . . . . . . . . . . . . . . . . . . . . . . . . . . . . . . . . . . . . . . . . . 61
Value-Added Versus Time Chart. . . . . . . . . . . . . . . . . . . . . . . . . . . . . . . . 62
The Eight Types of Waste . . . . . . . . . . . . . . . . . . . . . . . . . . . . . . . . . . . . . 64
Summary. . . . . . . . . . . . . . . . . . . . . . . . . . . . . . . . . . . . . . . . . . . . . . . . . . . 64
Endnotes . . . . . . . . . . . . . . . . . . . . . . . . . . . . . . . . . . . . . . . . . . . . . . . . . . . 66

**Chapter 6: Using the Language of Senior Management: The Bottom Line. . . . . . . . . .    67**

Introduction: Show Me the Money. . . . . . . . . . . . . . . . . . . . . . . . . . . . . . . . 67
The Externally Versus Internally Focused Organization . . . . . . . . . . . . . . . 69
Identify the Bottom Line . . . . . . . . . . . . . . . . . . . . . . . . . . . . . . . . . . . . . . 70
Cost of Quality Overview. . . . . . . . . . . . . . . . . . . . . . . . . . . . . . . . . . . . . . 77
Contributions of Cost of Quality . . . . . . . . . . . . . . . . . . . . . . . . . . . . . . . 78
Selling COQ to Leadership. . . . . . . . . . . . . . . . . . . . . . . . . . . . . . . . . . . . . 80
The Bottom Line Feeds Back to the Top Line: Use QFD to Validate VOC . . . . . . . . . 80
Endnotes . . . . . . . . . . . . . . . . . . . . . . . . . . . . . . . . . . . . . . . . . . . . . . . . . . . 81

**Chapter 7: Milestones and Measures: Interim and Final Reporting . . . . . . . . . . . . . . .    83**

Introduction. . . . . . . . . . . . . . . . . . . . . . . . . . . . . . . . . . . . . . . . . . . . . . . . . 83
Measurement Characteristics . . . . . . . . . . . . . . . . . . . . . . . . . . . . . . . . . . . 84
Improving Performance Is About Using Data . . . . . . . . . . . . . . . . . . . . . . . 89
Definitions in Support of Performance Management. . . . . . . . . . . . . . . . . . 90
Examples of the Four Components. . . . . . . . . . . . . . . . . . . . . . . . . . . . . . . 91
Does Your Agency Have a Performance Management System?. . . . . . . . . . . . 94
Performance Measures . . . . . . . . . . . . . . . . . . . . . . . . . . . . . . . . . . . . . . . . 95
Reporting of Progress . . . . . . . . . . . . . . . . . . . . . . . . . . . . . . . . . . . . . . . . . 95
The Performance Management Cycle . . . . . . . . . . . . . . . . . . . . . . . . . . . . . 96
Process Measures in Meso to Micro Level Department Activities. . . . . . . . . . 98
Endnotes . . . . . . . . . . . . . . . . . . . . . . . . . . . . . . . . . . . . . . . . . . . . . . . . . . . 99

**Chapter 8: Lean-Six Sigma: "Faster, Better, Smarter" . . . . . . . . . . . . . . . . . . . . . . . .    101**

Rapid Cycle Change and Project Management . . . . . . . . . . . . . . . . . . . . . . 104
   *Faster* . . . . . . . . . . . . . . . . . . . . . . . . . . . . . . . . . . . . . . . . . . . . . . . . . 104
   *Better* . . . . . . . . . . . . . . . . . . . . . . . . . . . . . . . . . . . . . . . . . . . . . . . . . 106
   *Smarter*. . . . . . . . . . . . . . . . . . . . . . . . . . . . . . . . . . . . . . . . . . . . . . . . 107
Combining Lean and Six Sigma Methods and Benefits. . . . . . . . . . . . . . . . 109
The DMAIC Methodology . . . . . . . . . . . . . . . . . . . . . . . . . . . . . . . . . . . . 110
Summary. . . . . . . . . . . . . . . . . . . . . . . . . . . . . . . . . . . . . . . . . . . . . . . . . . 116
Endnotes . . . . . . . . . . . . . . . . . . . . . . . . . . . . . . . . . . . . . . . . . . . . . . . . . . 117

**Chapter 9: The House of Lean-Six Sigma Tools and Techniques . . . . . . . . . . . . . . . .    119**

Building Blocks of House of Lean . . . . . . . . . . . . . . . . . . . . . . . . . . . . . . . 123
Steps into the House of Lean . . . . . . . . . . . . . . . . . . . . . . . . . . . . . . . . . . 129
The Foundation in the House of Lean . . . . . . . . . . . . . . . . . . . . . . . . . . . 129

The Roof for House of Lean............................................. 130
Summary............................................................. 130
Endnotes............................................................ 130

**Chapter 10: Incremental Versus Redesign Strategies.** ....................... **131**
   *Phase 1—Focus* ................................................ *135*
   *Phase 2—Assessment*........................................... *135*
   *Phase 3—Negotiation* ......................................... *136*
   *Phase 4—Redesign*............................................ *137*
   *Phase 5—Implementation* ...................................... *138*
Summary............................................................. 139
   *Laws of Core Process Redesign*................................. *140*
Endnotes............................................................ 140

**Chapter 11: Developing the QFD Team.** .................................. **143**
Types of Teams....................................................... 144
The Value of Teams to QFD ........................................... 147
Preparing Individuals to Be Effective Team Members...................... 149
Develop Individuals into an Effective Team............................. 150
Team Decision Making................................................. 153
The Decision-Making Process .......................................... 153
Attributes of a Good Decision ........................................ 155
Influence and Control Issues for Team Effectiveness...................... 156
   *The Problem Statement as a Vehicle for Norming*................. *158*
Develop Measures to Maintain Process Improvement ...................... 159
Set the Time Frame for Implementation................................. 160
   *Establish a Communication Plan*................................ *161*
Summary............................................................. 163
Endnotes............................................................ 164

**Chapter 12: Conducting a QFD Study.** .................................. **165**

**Chapter 13: Navigating the QFD Matrices** ............................... **173**
Endnotes............................................................ 182

**Appendix A: The Matrix of Matrices** ..................................... **183**

**Appendix B: QFD Software** ............................................. **185**

**Appendix C: List of QFD Reference Books.** .............................. **187**

**About the Authors** ................................................... **189**

**Index** .............................................................. **191**

# Figures and Tables

**Figure 1.1**  Continuous quality improvement system in public health. . . . . . . . . . . . . .  **2**

**Figure 1.2**  MPHCQI model for improvement . . . . . . . . . . . . . . . . . . . . . . . . . . . . . . . . .  **3**

**Figure 1.3**  Chart for lobby wait time, Dakota County Health
Department WIC program . . . . . . . . . . . . . . . . . . . . . . . . . . . . . . . . . . . .  **5**

**Figure 1.4**  General approach to use the basic tools of quality improvement . . . . . . . . .  **9**

**Figure 1.5**  General approach to use the advanced tools of quality improvement . . . . . .  **10**

**Figure 1.6**  Carver County local alert confirmation test flowchart . . . . . . . . . . . . . . . . .  **11**

**Figure 1.7**  Carver County local alert confirmation test cause and effect . . . . . . . . . . . .  **12**

**Figure 1.8**  Future state flowchart of optimized HAN test notification . . . . . . . . . . . . . .  **14**

**Figure 1.9**  Continuous quality improvement system in public health. . . . . . . . . . . . . . .  **15**

**Figure 2.1**  Process flow comparisons of predecessor methodologies . . . . . . . . . . . . . . .  **24**

**Figure 3.1**  The QFD/VOC integrated fulfillment approach . . . . . . . . . . . . . . . . . . . . . . .  **28**

**Figure 3.2**  General model of process-based health department performance . . . . . . . . .  **29**

**Figure 3.3**  The integration of technology, infrastructure, and personnel . . . . . . . . . . . .  **34**

**Figure 3.4**  The mechanics of an integrated approach to QI . . . . . . . . . . . . . . . . . . . . . . .  **35**

**Figure 4.1**  Client relationship model . . . . . . . . . . . . . . . . . . . . . . . . . . . . . . . . . . . . . . .  **38**

**Figure 4.2**  Which process steps impact customer needs? . . . . . . . . . . . . . . . . . . . . . . . .  **40**

**Figure 4.3**  Cause and effect diagram of poor customer service . . . . . . . . . . . . . . . . . . .  **41**

**Figure 4.4**  Factors to obtain the VOC . . . . . . . . . . . . . . . . . . . . . . . . . . . . . . . . . . . . . . .  **43**

**Figure 4.5**  Kano model . . . . . . . . . . . . . . . . . . . . . . . . . . . . . . . . . . . . . . . . . . . . . . . . . .  **44**

**Figure 4.6**  Understanding/interpreting the voice of the customer. . . . . . . . . . . . . . . . . .  **45**

**Figure 4.7**  Understand the overlapping, conflicting, and distinct needs of each
customer group. . . . . . . . . . . . . . . . . . . . . . . . . . . . . . . . . . . . . . . . . . . . . .  **46**

**Figure 5.1**  Basic symbols for a process map. . . . . . . . . . . . . . . . . . . . . . . . . . . . . . . . . .  **52**

**Figure 5.2**  Basic process map for childhood immunization clinic . . . . . . . . . . . . . . . . .  **53**

**Figure 5.3**    Opportunity flowchart for childhood immunization clinic . . . . . . . . . . . . . **56**

**Figure 5.4**    Flowchart symbols for value stream mapping . . . . . . . . . . . . . . . . . . . . . . **58**

**Figure 5.5**    Current state value stream map for childhood immunization clinic . . . . . . . **60**

**Figure 5.6**    Future state value stream map for childhood immunization clinic . . . . . . . . **61**

**Figure 5.7**    Spaghetti diagram for a patient at childhood immunization clinic . . . . . . . . **62**

**Figure 5.8**    Spaghetti diagram for a provider at childhood immunization clinic . . . . . . . **63**

**Figure 5.9**    Value-added versus time chart . . . . . . . . . . . . . . . . . . . . . . . . . . . . . . . **63**

**Figure 6.1**    Initial projection of annual operating budget expenses . . . . . . . . . . . . . . . **68**

**Figure 6.2**    Externally versus internally focused costing approaches . . . . . . . . . . . . . . **70**

**Figure 6.3**    Soaring Eagle Clinic 2010 operating statement . . . . . . . . . . . . . . . . . . . . . **71**

**Figure 6.4**    Orange County Health Department immunization map . . . . . . . . . . . . . . . **73**

**Figure 6.5**    OCHD child immunization process costing summary worksheet . . . . . . . . . **76**

**Figure 6.6**    OCHD immunization flowchart process costing with COQ estimates . . . . . **79**

**Figure 7.1**    Client requirements to design requirements . . . . . . . . . . . . . . . . . . . . . . . **84**

**Figure 7.2**    Florida Department of Children and Families QFD customer
requirements to design requirements (partial) . . . . . . . . . . . . . . . . . . . . . . **86**

**Figure 7.3**    Control plan for DCF customer to design requirements QFD matrix . . . . . . **87**

**Figure 7.4**    Performance management framework and components . . . . . . . . . . . . . . . **90**

**Figure 7.5**    Orange County Health Department current state process map . . . . . . . . . . **92**

**Figure 7.6**    Flowchart summary form for septic system permitting QI project . . . . . . . . **93**

**Figure 7.7**    Introduction to the Pennsylvania Department of Health
Intranet site for data driven management . . . . . . . . . . . . . . . . . . . . . . . . . . **96**

**Figure 7.8**    Conceptual framework of the public health system as a basis
for measuring public health systems performance . . . . . . . . . . . . . . . . . . . **98**

**Figure 8.1**    Evolution of Lean-Six Sigma methodologies . . . . . . . . . . . . . . . . . . . . . . **103**

**Figure 8.2**    Relationship of QFD and LSS approaches for quality improvement . . . . . . **108**

**Figure 8.3**    The DMAIC methodology . . . . . . . . . . . . . . . . . . . . . . . . . . . . . . . . . . . **111**

**Figure 8.4**    Percent nondefective under a normal curve using Six Sigma concept . . . . . **114**

**Figure 8.5**    Performance metrics developed from customer requirements . . . . . . . . . . . **115**

**Figure 9.1**    The PDCA continuous improvement cycle . . . . . . . . . . . . . . . . . . . . . . . . **120**

**Figure 9.2**    General approach using the basic tools of quality improvement . . . . . . . . . **120**

**Figure 9.3**    General approach to using the advanced tools of quality improvement . . . . **121**

**Figure 9.4**    LSS DMAIC management system . . . . . . . . . . . . . . . . . . . . . . . . . . . . . . **122**

**Figure 9.5**    The house of lean. . . . . . . . . . . . . . . . . . . . . . . . . . . . . . . . . . . . . .    **123**

**Figure 9.6**    Spaghetti diagram showing health department
administrative office flow. . . . . . . . . . . . . . . . . . . . . . . . . . . . . . . .    **126**

**Figure 9.7**    Current state value stream map environmental data . . . . . . . . . . . . . . . . . .    **128**

**Figure 10.1**    Types of improvement . . . . . . . . . . . . . . . . . . . . . . . . . . . . . . . . . . . .    **132**

**Figure 10.2**    Six areas critical for successful business outcomes. . . . . . . . . . . . . . . . . . .    **133**

**Figure 10.3**    The CPR pathway . . . . . . . . . . . . . . . . . . . . . . . . . . . . . . . . . . . . . . .    **135**

**Figure 10.4**    Transitional time line. . . . . . . . . . . . . . . . . . . . . . . . . . . . . . . . . . . . .    **139**

**Figure 11.1**    The four houses of quality . . . . . . . . . . . . . . . . . . . . . . . . . . . . . . . . .    **150**

**Figure 11.2**    Voice of the customer to voice of the process . . . . . . . . . . . . . . . . . . . . . .    **152**

**Figure 11.3**    Teams make decisions for continuous improvement. . . . . . . . . . . . . . . . . .    **154**

**Figure 11.4**    Layers of team control and influence. . . . . . . . . . . . . . . . . . . . . . . . . . .    **156**

**Figure 11.5**    Components of the issue . . . . . . . . . . . . . . . . . . . . . . . . . . . . . . . . . . .    **157**

**Figure 11.6**    Internal versus external focus . . . . . . . . . . . . . . . . . . . . . . . . . . . . . . .    **158**

**Figure 11.7**    Operational versus strategic issue . . . . . . . . . . . . . . . . . . . . . . . . . . . .    **159**

**Figure 11.8**    Process, capacity, outcomes measurement. . . . . . . . . . . . . . . . . . . . . . . .    **160**

**Figure 11.9**    Measurement examples for performance. . . . . . . . . . . . . . . . . . . . . . . . .    **161**

**Figure 11.10**    Gantt chart for implementation time line. . . . . . . . . . . . . . . . . . . . . . . .    **162**

**Figure 11.11**    Sample communication plan . . . . . . . . . . . . . . . . . . . . . . . . . . . . . . . .    **163**

**Figure 12.1**    L-shaped matrix. . . . . . . . . . . . . . . . . . . . . . . . . . . . . . . . . . . . . . . .    **166**

**Figure 12.2**    M × N matrix . . . . . . . . . . . . . . . . . . . . . . . . . . . . . . . . . . . . . . . . .    **166**

**Figure 12.3**    Tree diagram . . . . . . . . . . . . . . . . . . . . . . . . . . . . . . . . . . . . . . . . . .    **167**

**Figure 12.4**    The system-level QFD approach . . . . . . . . . . . . . . . . . . . . . . . . . . . . . .    **168**

**Figure 12.5**    Four houses of quality . . . . . . . . . . . . . . . . . . . . . . . . . . . . . . . . . . . .    **168**

**Figure 12.6**    House of quality. . . . . . . . . . . . . . . . . . . . . . . . . . . . . . . . . . . . . . . .    **169**

**Figure 12.7**    Translating the "who" to the "how". . . . . . . . . . . . . . . . . . . . . . . . . . . .    **170**

**Figure 13.1**    Chart A-1: The house of quality. . . . . . . . . . . . . . . . . . . . . . . . . . . . . .    **174**

**Figure 13.2**    VOC tree diagram . . . . . . . . . . . . . . . . . . . . . . . . . . . . . . . . . . . . . .    **175**

**Figure 13.3**    Solution and effect diagram. . . . . . . . . . . . . . . . . . . . . . . . . . . . . . . . .    **177**

**Figure 13.4**    Technical characteristics tree diagram. . . . . . . . . . . . . . . . . . . . . . . . . .    **178**

**Figure 13.5**    Four houses of quality . . . . . . . . . . . . . . . . . . . . . . . . . . . . . . . . . . . .    **180**

**Table 1.1**    Dakota County Public Health Department WIC program
process improvement project overview . . . . . . . . . . . . . . . . . . . . . . . . . . .    **4**

**Table 1.2**    Macro, Meso, Micro, and Individual mapped to Big, Little, and Individual QI. . . . . . . . . . . . . . . . . . . . . . . . . . . . . . . . . . . .    **7**

**Table 1.3**    PDSA—Carver County HAN alert system tests of change . . . . . . . . . . . . .    **13**

**Table 5.1**    Eight types of waste . . . . . . . . . . . . . . . . . . . . . . . . . . . . . . . . . . . . . . . . . .    **65**

**Table 8.1**    Lean-Six Sigma roles and responsibilities . . . . . . . . . . . . . . . . . . . . . . . . .    **112**

**Table 9.1**    Categories and descriptions of 5S for septic permit program . . . . . . . . . . .    **124**

**Table 13.1**    A-1 Matrix for weighted customer importance . . . . . . . . . . . . . . . . . . . . . .    **176**

**Table 13.2**    Component D: House of quality weighting of whats and hows . . . . . . . . . .    **179**

**Table 13.3**    Matrix to calculate measurement targets for product or service outcomes . . . . . . . . . . . . . . . . . . . . . . . . . . . . . . . . . . . . . . . . . .    **181**

# Preface

*Ron Bialek, President, Public Health Foundation*

Public Health has recognized the value of continuous improvement. Quality improvement (QI) teams are engaged across the country in identifying root causes of the issues that prevent us from providing the best Public Health services to communities and individuals. We are seeing tremendous excitement throughout the country around the use of QI tools and techniques. Public Health agencies and systems are learning these techniques, exploring and experimenting with them, and developing new and even better approaches to Public Health QI. And yes, we are seeing results: improved processes, efficiencies, and community health status.

The release of *The Quality Improvement Handbook for Public Health* in 2009 signaled a coming together of the best minds in the industry around the current and future state of Public Health performance excellence. Health departments across the nation are using the basic quality tools to assess the needs of their communities, identify priority areas for improvement, and implement processes and measures to meet those needs in a reliable manner.

These foundation efforts are making a difference. Public Health professionals form cross-functional teams with other agencies and not-for-profit organizations to balance resources and share skills to meet the broader needs of the total community. Public Health support organizations such as the Public Health Foundation publish success stories and papers forming the basis of new research in QI methods for community health services.

There is still much more to be done. Comparing the health of the United States with the rest of the world and the health of most every community, we know that we can do better. The public and policy makers are demanding better health outcomes and more efficient use of scarce resources.

The tools of quality, when used effectively, will truly make a difference in the public's health. The basic tools of quality, anchored by the Plan-Do-Check/Study-Act cycle, are helping Public Health departments improve processes at the local level. It is time to take a more advanced approach for cross functional and long-term improvements that will achieve the systems level results we desire and the public deserves.

Central to the mission of the Public Health Foundation is helping Public Health agencies and systems achieve measurable improvement and better results. This text, introducing quality function deployment (QFD) and Lean-Six Sigma (LSS), is a valuable next step for the integration of improved community health outcomes. We know from years of experience working with Public Health agencies and systems that there are common requirements for Public Health services across the nation. There also are unique needs of individual communities.

The matrixed approach of QFD acknowledges specific priorities of a unique audience. Traditional inputs to health and environmental needs, such as community assessments, regional trend analysis or projections of future growth, feed directly into the voice of the customer process that is the gateway for QFD.

LSS offers a broader range of techniques beyond the seven basic tools of QI now in frequent use among Public Health and community service organizations. The authors provide the next level of quality for both strategic leadership and operational QI teams ready to move beyond the entry level of performance and measurement techniques. This book is written by professionals who are actively using the advanced tools of quality and coaching leading-edge teams for maximum results.

The methods in this text are the next step for us to harness the energy, enthusiasm, hard work, and dedication of our Public Health workforce to make a lasting difference. By effectively expanding our use of QI tools and techniques, we can and will improve our nation's health and the health of the many communities we serve.

# Acknowledgments

The application of process-based improvement in Public Health is an exciting new field. The authors are privileged to work with a number of Public Health professionals as we push the envelope for using the quality tools to support community needs. The following professionals and their related Health Departments have been critical in the application of quality function deployment and Lean-Six Sigma in Public Health situations. The authors are grateful for their involvement in this significant project.

**Orange County Health Department, Orlando, Florida**

Strategic planning manager:
James E. Pate

Quality manager:
Vicente Alberto Araujo

Lean-Six Sigma project managers:
Shelly Persaud
Anne Marie Strickland
Susannah Mena
Melissa Hulse

Data Analyst:
Andrew Burns

**Minnesota Department of Health**

Kim McCoy, MS, MPH: principal planning specialist

**University of Minnesota, School of Public Health**

Mac McCullough, BS, research assistant and MPH student, University of Minnesota School of Public Health.

Ben Smalley, research assistant and MHA/MBA student, University of Minnesota School of Public Health and Carlson School of Business

Finally, the authors are eternally grateful to our ASQ Quality Press editors, Matt Meinholz and Paul O'Mara, for believing in us when we approached them with the value of quality improvement in Public Health. The future of health is in prevention, not just clinical treatment of existing conditions. Healthy processes support healthy behaviors. May our readers benefit from the connection.

# Introduction

The purpose of this book is to introduce the concepts embedded in quality function deployment (QFD) and Lean-Six Sigma to help Public Health professionals implement quality improvement within their agencies. The tools and techniques of QFD and Lean-Six Sigma are designed to augment a robust PDCA or PDSA problem-solving process, not replace it.

The tools and techniques of QFD and Lean-Six Sigma can help problem-solving teams by providing insight into customer needs and wants, design and development of customer-centric processes, and mapping value streams. Both QFD and Lean-Six Sigma focus on doing the most with the resources we have. Each of these megatools supports efforts to expand our community support programs and to increase the effectiveness of internal capacities. This dual external/internal focus offers an excellent partnership of quality improvement tools for Public Health.

The tools and techniques of QFD and Lean-Six Sigma can help a problem-solving team make breakthrough improvements by building in customer requirements early in the problem-solving process as well as setting the stage for future improvements. You will find that the QFD process ensures that the voice of the customer (VOC) drives all activities associated with designing or redesigning a product or service for internal or external customers. Lean-Six Sigma uses the same VOC inputs to align every activity within the Public Health department (PHD) directly with stated needs of the community and its stakeholders. These two methodologies will help improve quality, costs, and timeliness of products and services, which in for-profit businesses translates into increased profitability. In Public Health, having lower costs can mean more can be done with existing budget dollars.

The objectives of QFD and Lean-Six Sigma are as follows:

- Provide higher-quality products and services to customers.

- Achieve customer-driven design of these products and services by converting user needs into design parameters

- Provide documentation and tracking system for future design endeavors

- Develop delivery processes that are efficient and effective

- Involve suppliers early in the process

- Require data-driven decision making and incorporate a comprehensive set of quality tools under a powerful framework for effective problem-solving

- Provide tools for analyzing process flow and delay times at each activity in a process

The early results of the use of QFD in the United States included a reduction in the cycle time for design work, a defining of quality early in the design stage, a decrease in quality problems during manufacturing, a way to objectively bench-mark against the competition on improvements, reduced warranty claims, and an improvement in cross-functional team work.

In this book we will modify the QFD process and Lean-Six Sigma methodology so they are aligned with the needs and differences in Public Health design and delivery of products and services. When we make modifications we will point this out so readers will understand the change from what might be seen in an industrial or healthcare application of the same concepts.

# 1

# The Continuum of Quality Improvement in Public Health

## INTRODUCTION

As the Public Health community expands its use of quality improvement (QI), there is often confusion about how all the tools, techniques, methodologies, models, and approaches fit together.[1] Available techniques include basic and advanced tools of quality improvement as well as several QI models including quality function deployment, Lean-Six Sigma, daily management, mobilizing for action through planning and partnerships (MAPP),[2] turning point,[3] Baldrige,[4] and state quality award models. At times, these models are introduced as competing techniques and processes. The models are not tied together into a system by which they complement one another. This chapter provides an overview showing how various QI techniques and improvement models are related to one another and can be used in compatible ways. The Public Health community would benefit from an overall approach that completely integrates QI into its management practices. Continuous improvement is one component of an integrated system of performance management by which an organization meets and exceeds the needs and expectations of its multiple customer, client, and stakeholder communities.

Some of the ways in which performance management can positively influence a Public Health agency are:

- Better return on dollars invested in health

- Greater accountability for funding and increases in the public's trust

- Reduced duplication of efforts

- Better understanding of Public Health accomplishments and priorities among employees, partners, and the public

- Increased sense of cooperation and teamwork

- Increased emphasis on quality, rather than quantity

- Improved problem solving[5]

More on performance management as an approach to improved community support is provided in Chapter 7.

The Accreditation Coalition Quality Improvement Subgroup[6] reached a consensus on March 26, 2009, that defined quality improvement in Public Health and that was approved by the Accreditation Coalition in June 2009:

> *Quality improvement in public health is the use of a deliberate and defined improvement process, such as plan-do-check-act, which is focused on activities that are responsive to community needs and improving population health.*
>
> *It refers to a continuous and ongoing effort to achieve measurable improvements in the efficiency, effectiveness, performance, accountability, outcomes, and other indicators of quality in services or processes which achieve equity and improve the health of the community*

As shown in Figure 1.1, QI in Public Health is a never-ending process that pervades the organization when fully implemented. Top organizational leaders address the quality of the system at a Macro level (Big "QI"). In the middle, professional staff attacks problems in programs or service areas by improving particular processes (Little "qi"). At the individual level, staff seeks ways of improving their own behaviors and environments (Individual "qi").

When starting their quality journey, Public Health organizations tend to embrace Little "qi," which means striving for quality in a limited or specific improvement project or area. This is accomplished by using an integrated set of QI methods and techniques that create a value map, identify the key quality characteristics, analyze process performance, reengineer the process if needed, and lock in improve-

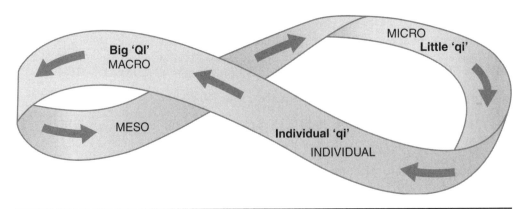

**Figure 1.1**   Continuous quality improvement system in public health.

ments. Little "qi" can be viewed as a tactical or systems approach to implementing quality and beginning to generate a culture of QI within the organization.[7]

## PROCESS IMPROVEMENT IN A PUBLIC HEALTH DEPARTMENT

The model for improvement[8] is one of several approaches that can be used in Public Health departments. As shown in Figure 1.2, the model for improvement consists of several components, including: setting an aim statement, developing measures, implementing tests of change, and using the plan-do-study-act (PDSA) cycle.

## LITTLE "qi"

Thingstad-Boe, Riley, and Parsons[9] recently reported an example of using the model for improvement to demonstrate the application of Little "qi" in a Women,

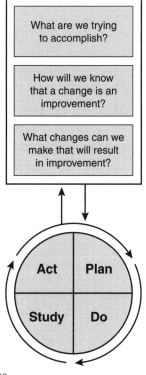

1. Define the problem
2. Set an aim
3. Establish measures of progress
4. Develop an action plan
5. Test interventions
6. Monitor progress and evaluate results
7. Implement changes

Source: IHI, 1998.

**Figure 1.2**    MPHCQI model for improvement.

Infants, and Children (WIC) program of a county Public Health department in Minnesota. The WIC program is an important nutrition program created in 1966 by the federal government to address concerns about the impact of inadequate nutrition during critical periods of fetal infant and child growth and development.[10] The QI project was conducted in the state's third largest county, which has an annual WIC caseload of more than 70,000 clients.

The study was carried out using the model for improvement. Table 1.1 shows how the four components were used: setting the aim in specific terms, establishing measures to indicate whether a change actually would lead to program improvements, developing general ideas for change that could stimulate specific changes leading to improvements, and applying a plan-do-study-act cycle to test and implement changes. After approval from top leadership, a QI team was established, and it collected initial data regarding the clinic's baseline process performance and client satisfaction. The team then created a value stream map to illustrate the current process and used a control chart to analyze current process performance levels. Upon determining that the process was stable but not capable of meeting client's expectations, the team applied statistical process control analysis to re-engineer the process. Follow-up data demonstrated that the reengineered process led to improved performance, so the team locked in the new process based on these data.

The absence of special cause (a specific factor that causes variation in process performance) in lobby wait time in the process analysis phase of the study led the improvement team to focus on process reengineering rather than process improvement (*process improvement* is removing the special cause, while *process reengineering* involves a complete overhaul of a process). The intervention consisted of creating revised floor travel patterns, redeploying personnel, and conducting staff training to achieve client goals. The results of the Little "qi" project are shown in the X-bar chart in Figure 1.3 (the moving range chart is not shown). The control chart shows the initial process performance for 10 consecutive clinic days at the beginning of the study and 14 consecutive days after the process was

**Table 1.1**   Dakota County Public Health Department WIC program process improvement project overview.

| Aim statement | Improve client satisfaction in county health department WIC Program in six months |
|---|---|
| Measures of change | Decrease lobby wait time by 20%; increase client satisfaction scale by 25% |
| Change concept | Reengineer the WIC service process |
| PDSA cycle | Analyze process, create value stream map, eliminate non-value-added steps, pilot new process, document process shift, and lock in change |

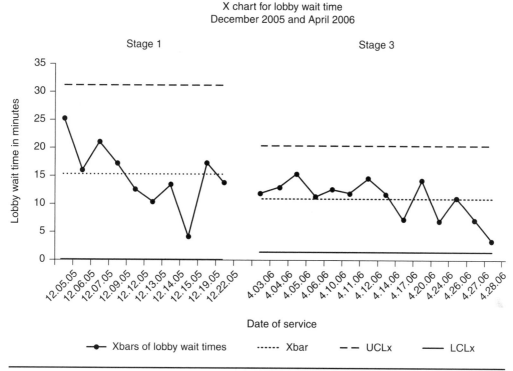

**Figure 1.3**    Chart for lobby wait time, Dakota County Health Department WIC program.[11]

redesigned. The break in the center line reflects the process shift that occurred between the pre-intervention and post-intervention process performances. The control chart shows a mean reduction in waiting time from 15.1 minutes to 10.9 minutes (a 28% decrease). The study also found that client satisfaction increased 20% as a result of reduced lobby wait time.

## BIG "QI"

Long wait times in WIC clinics have been shown to be a significant barrier to picking up food vouchers,[12] while shorter wait times have been shown to enhance clients' overall experience.[13] This example demonstrates the importance of designing processes that minimize or eliminate client service barriers. It also emphasizes the pressure in Public Health departments to increase efficiency and look for ways to use program resources more effectively to reduce wait times, creating improved access.

Big "QI" can be viewed as a strategic or macro systems approach to implementing quality. Integration of QI processes into daily work and agency-wide performance management is often driven by implementation of frameworks such as MAPP, the Baldrige Criteria, Lean, and turning point. Leaders must be deliberate and persistent in their efforts to push QI throughout the organization until it becomes part of the culture and practice. Big "QI" refers to the practice of striving for excellence in all of an organization's services, products, processes, and overall operations, making it a top management philosophy resulting in complete organizational involvement in quality.

The Dakota County Public Health Department example highlights the movement toward Big "QI" in Public Health departments. The health department senior management gave initial approval to start the process improvement project and supported all phases of the undertaking.[14] As organizations become knowledgeable and more experienced with QI and as leaders and staff witness the results of Little "qi" efforts, they are likely to seek ways to expand the impact of QI to more parts of the organization.

## LARGE-SCALE PUBLIC HEALTH SYSTEM QUALITY IMPROVEMENT

The QI project undertaken in the WIC program is an example of QI at the *organizational level*. Building a QI capacity in Public Health also needs to be done at the large scale *system level*. At Public Health system level, the authors are involved in integrating the Macro, Meso, Micro, Individual model of continuous QI within a number of Public Health organizations at the local, state, and regional levels. For example, the Minnesota Public Health Collaborative for Quality Improvement[15] provides a framework for beginning to build a QI culture in a state Public Health system.

The Macro level of the continuous quality improvement (CQI) system shown in Figure 1.1 is the strategic integration of long-term approaches to meet overall priority outcomes of the Public Health system. The Macro level involves an emphasis throughout the entire organization. The Meso level contains the planning and deployment of programs that translate strategic vision and long-range outcomes into specific programs and departments within the health department. The Micro level encompasses the health department projects and programs instituted at the functional unit level.

Table 1.2 shows how the Macro, Meso, Micro, and Individual levels of the CQI System model relate to Big "QI," Little "qi," and Individual "qi." The Meso level of the CQI system model overlays both the Macro and Micro level as a transition for deployment from organizational to unit-specific projects. Table 1.2 also suggests the use of basic and advanced tools of quality within the scope of organization versus unit activities. The basic QI tools, such as flowcharts and histograms, are most useful in addressing more quantitative and

**Table 1.2** Macro, Meso, Micro, and Individual mapped to Big, Little, and Individual QI.

| Topic | Big 'QI'—organization-wide | | Little 'qi'—program/unit | | Individual 'qi' |
|---|---|---|---|---|---|
| *System level* ⟶<br>*Quality tools* ⟶ | *Macro*<br>Advanced | *Meso*<br>QFD/Lean Six Sigma | *Micro* | Basic | *Individual* |
| Improvement | System focus | | Specific project focus | | Daily work level focus |
| Quality improvement planning | Tied to the strategic plan | | Program/unit level | | Tied to yearly individual performance |
| Evaluation of quality processes | Responsiveness to a community need | | Performance of a process over time | | Performance of daily work |
| Quality improvement goals | Cut across all programs and activities<br><br>Strategic plan | | Delivery of a service<br><br>Individual program/unit level plans | | Daily work<br><br>Individual performance plans |

tangible issues of immediate problem solving. The advanced tools of quality use more behavioral and decision-making tools, such as force field analysis and interrelationship digraphs. The Meso CQI System level uses even more flexible tools such as quality function deployment and Lean-Six Sigma to provide structure for translating customer needs into specific actions and tasks for problem solving and improvement. The Individual system level uses any tools that support the specific task, although the basic tools are most often employed.

An example of Large Scale Public Health System QI improvement is the Minnesota Public Health Collaborative for Quality Improvement (MPHCQI), a statewide QI collaborative supported by grants from the Robert Wood Johnson Foundation. Minnesota has 87 counties and encompasses 11 Native American tribal entities. Seventy-five local health departments and 53 community health boards serve communities across the state.[16] A State Community Health Services Advisory Committee includes representatives of each community health board and advises the commissioner of health.[17]

The Minnesota Department of Health, in partnership with local health departments, established 40 essential local activities that define what every resident of Minnesota should be able to expect from their local health department. These activities are organized into six areas of Public Health responsibility. These Micro-level local activities are monitored at the Macro (senior management) level, according to the continuous improvement model in Figure 1.1. The monitoring is accomplished with annual reporting through the Planning and Performance Measurement Reporting System (PPMRS) operated by the Minnesota Department of Health.[18]

The reporting system provides data that describe local Public Health operations including:

- Programs and functions
- Budgets
- Staffing and capacity

At the Macro level the Minnesota Department of Health coordinates a five- year local assessment and planning process that is mandated by statute to facilitate achievement of the desired statewide outcomes for each of the six areas of Public Health responsibility.

At the national level, the Minnesota Department of Health joins 15 other state programs in the Multi-State Learning Collaborative (MLC), funded by the Robert Wood Johnson Foundation.[19] The MLC was established in 2006 and is targeted to end in 2011 with the kickoff of a nationwide system of performance management and Public Health system accreditation. The goals of the MLC are to advance accreditation and quality improvement strategies in Public Health departments. The goal of the Robert Wood Johnson Foundation and the Public Health Accreditation Board[20] is for 60% of the U.S. population to be served by an accredited health department by 2015.

Minnesota joined the MLC in 2007 during the second phase of activities. The Minnesota Public Health Collaborative for Quality Improvement (MPHCQI) was established as a partnership among the Minnesota Department of Health, the Local Public Health Association, and the University of Minnesota School of Public Health. The goals of the MPHCQI are:

- To build Public Health workforce capacity to use quality improvement tools and methods
- To establish a performance management system that is aligned with the national accreditation standards

The MPHCQI organized eight projects that involved 34 local health departments to test a systematic integration of quality tools and techniques based on the model for improvement[21] seen in Figure 1.2. The model for improvement is a data-based approach with a repeatable process for improvement and a strategic foundation for benchmarking and accreditation, which is the overall goal of the MPHCQI and the national MLC.

Senior leaders ensure that an organization understands the priority areas of focus for improvement, a feature of the Meso system level shown in Figure 1.1. At the Meso level there needs to be clear problem statements so those assigned to work on the priority issues understand the importance and scope of their assignment. The problem statement should clearly indicate whether the project and problem to be solved are specific to a program/unit or are organization-wide.

The Meso system model of PDCA or PDSA links two general approaches on how to use the basic and advanced tools of quality. These two general models are shown in Figures 1.4 and 1.5. Normally the program- or unit-specific problems start with the basic tools of quality to determine the root cause of the problem as seen in Figure 1.4. Organization-wide problems generally require the advanced tools of quality, as shown in Figure 1.5, to solve the problem.

Once the type of problem to be solved is identified, the tools to use are described in the sequence that they are typically applied. Clear articulation of the problem statement is the first step in the MPHCQI framework in Figure 1.2.

As mentioned earlier, continuous improvement is accomplished by using an integrated set of QI methods and techniques that create a value map, identify the key quality characteristics, analyze process performance, re-engineer the process if needed, and lock in improvements. Figure 1.6 is an example of a flowchart to identify the current state of a process supporting the local health alert network (HAN) prepared by a QI team from the health department in Carver County, Minnesota. What began at the Micro level as a "Little qi" opportunity to reduce cycle time and rework at the local level quickly became a Meso level project by considering the impact of the local alert confirmation test shared across all the health departments within the state. This common process was more standardized, rather than being performed in different ways across the Minnesota Health Alert Network.

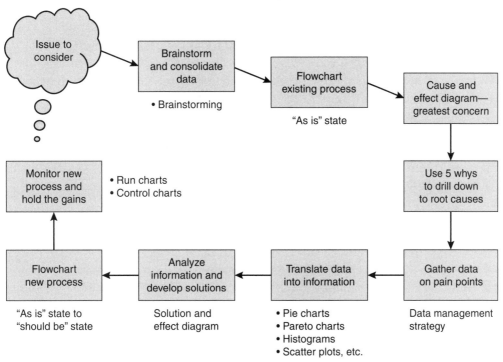

Source: *The Public Health Quality Improvement Handbook*, R. Bialek, G. Duffy, J. Moran, Editors, Quality Press, © 2009, p.160.

**Figure 1.4**  General approach to use the basic tools of quality improvement.

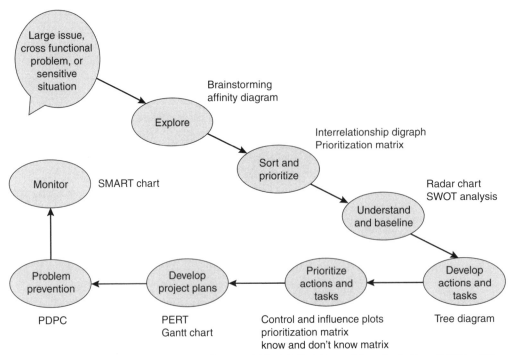

Source: *The Public Health Quality Improvement Handbook*, R. Bialek, G. Duffy, J. Moran, Editors, Quality Press, © 2009, p.160.

**Figure 1.5**   General approach to use the advanced tools of quality improvement.

The current state map (flowchart) in Figure 1.6 enabled the QI team to develop the problem statement and a cause and effect diagram shown in Figure 1.7. The brainstorming of issues involved with conducting the HAN test led to an affinity exercise to identify five symptom categories related to the problem statement of "Too much staff time to conduct HAN test":

- Policies

- Procedures

- Plant/technology

- Measurement

- People

Analysis of the symptoms listed in the cause and effect diagram shown in Figure 1.7 led to the selection of three priority opportunities for improvement. Table 1.3 identifies the three interventions chosen by the Carver County improvement team and the resulting changes to the Alert Test process.

As noted in Table 1.3, one intervention, that of assigning two people to log replies from the locations receiving the test alert, made no change in the cycle time (length of time to complete a process step) of the activity. The two other

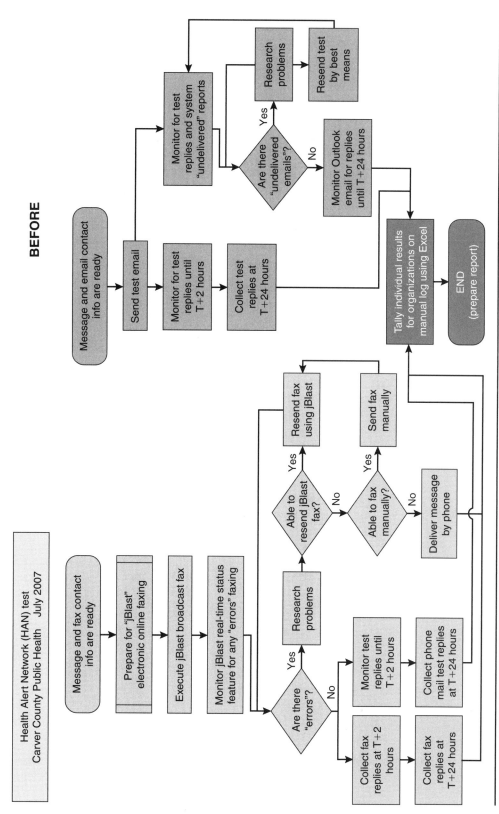

**Figure 1.6**  Carver County local alert confirmation test flowchart.

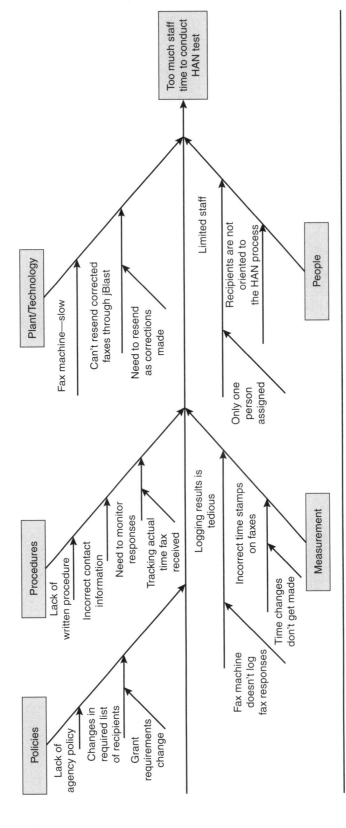

**Figure 1.7**    Carver County local alert confirmation test cause and effect.

**Table 1.3**   PDSA—Carver County HAN alert system tests of change.

| Intervention | Result |
| --- | --- |
| Two people logging replies | No change in staff time |
| Streamlined Excel spreadheet | Decrease of 2 hours |
| Revised reply form (email and fax) and decreased monitoring of faxes | Decrease of 5 hours |

interventions listed in the PDSA table decreased the cycle time of the test process by 2 and 5 hours respectively. Figure 1.8 represents a process redesign that resulted in a 70% decrease in staff time devoted to a HAN test.

QI in an organization can start top down, bottom up, or both simultaneously. As QI becomes the norm in an organization, it becomes more common for staff to use Individual "qi" in daily work. Daily management is the use of Individual "qi" to make improvements to daily work; in other words, it becomes a habit. Daily management is the overarching philosophy of incremental change in the day-to-day work we all do to meet the needs of the client and the community. It is a cornerstone of the Continuum of Quality Improvement in Public Health described in Figure 1.1. People doing the work make daily incremental improvements to constantly keep up with shifting public-health needs.[22]

# BIG "QI," LITTLE "qi," AND INDIVIDUAL "qi"

A transformational change is when QI is based on a comprehensive approach starting at the Macro-level Big "QI" using a model like turning point or Baldrige model that describes an overall method to manage a Public Health department. Table 1.2 illustrates three levels of QI (Big "QI," Little "qi," and Individual "qi") and lists five QI characteristics: improvement focus, quality improvement planning, evaluation of quality, analysis of processes, and quality improvement goals.

Big "QI" characteristics are focused on the organization as a whole. Little "qi" is viewed as the project or program level within a specific local Public Health department or, occasionally, across local departments serving a metropolitan area that overlaps several county and city borders. Individual "qi" reflects the earlier concept of daily management as practiced by the QI professionals within the scope of their work assignment.

Quality function deployment (QFD)[23] and Lean-Six Sigma (LSS)[24] are two additional QI methodologies that we introduce to this model. We position them between the Meso and Micro system levels to help expand the problem-solving ability of QI teams. QFD assists in capturing the voice of the community (VOC). The VOC consists of the community needs, determined through a needs

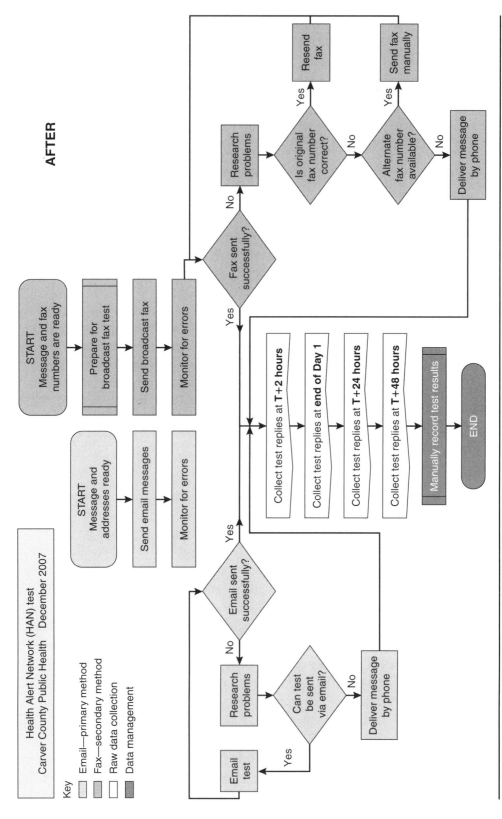

**Figure 1.8** Future state flowchart of optimized HAN test notification.

assessment, and translated into programs and services that address the community or internal user needs. Lean-Six Sigma is a methodology that integrates concepts and tools from lean enterprise and Six Sigma methodologies.

QFD identifies what is important to the community served by the health department and Lean-Six Sigma ensures that all available resources are directly engaged in the fulfillment of community needs. Lean activities maximize use of resources and minimize waste within all processes. The elimination of waste is a critical success factor in a resource-constrained environment. Lessons from competitive industries suggest there will always be better ways to do the same function for less, or faster, or better given the same use of resources. Six Sigma activities seek to reduce variation in delivery of products and services to meet customer expectations and needs.

## CONCLUSION

Figure 1.9 shows the entire Continuous Macro-Meso-Micro-Individual Quality Improvement System in Public Health and how tools, techniques, methodologies, and approaches fit together and support one another. A health department can start anywhere on this model, but as the QI capacity expands the department can move to a technique more appropriate for its needs.

The Minnesota Public Health Collaborative for Quality Improvement has so far contained efforts to the model for improvement described in Figure 1.2.

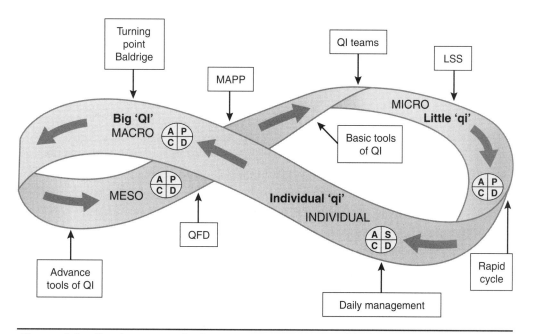

**Figure 1.9**   Continuous quality improvement system in public health.

Although this chapter reflects only one example of the projects undertaken by the MPHCQI as part of the Multi-State Learning Collaborative, the total endeavor consisted of eight projects. The results to date of the MPHCQI include:

- Approximately 250 state, local, and university Public Health professionals have been trained in 10 QI methods

- 34 local Public Health agencies across Minnesota have implemented QI projects

Improvement was achieved in seven of eight projects and shared with local Public Health departments across the state (one project made no improvement).[25] Of these seven projects, five projects achieved breakthrough improvement:

- 70% reduction in staff time devoted to Health Alert Network testing (the example offered in this chapter)

- Over 100% increase in leadership understanding of Public Health workforce competencies

- Over 100 children enrolled in a dental varnish treatment program

- 60% increase in timely completion of personal care assistant reassessments

- 169 children screened for behavioral health issues

Two of the eight projects achieved incremental improvement:

- 3% increase in immunizations for WIC (Women, Infants, and Children) clients, 6% increase for non-WIC clients

- Reduced number of forms for recording treatment of latent TB infection from 13 to 6

These projects are the target of continued evaluation for sustainability. Examples of this monitoring and control are: (1) self-administered surveys after each learning session, (2) self-administered online survey of 65 team members at conclusion of projects, (3) one-year follow-up interview of team leaders.

Minnesota Public Health quality professionals, as well as those in other states, are working with the authors of this text to incorporate the CQI System, including projects at the Macro, Meso, and Micro levels into their normal operating processes. Another series of Minnesota Public Health projects was started in 2009, with 130 QI teams across the state.

The continuous quality improvement system in Public Health model is showing health department professionals that QI methods can produce measurable change in delivery of local Public Health services. Slight adaptations to the traditional basic and advanced tools of quality make the model more amenable to public service settings by using the language of the Public Health professional. The successes realized in the projects presented in this chapter may not be generalizable to all Public Health systems. The evidence base will be expanded as more Public Health departments conduct QI initiatives.

# ENDNOTES

1. The authors wish to acknowledge the contribution of Kim McCoy, MPH, MS, CQIA, who is a principal planner with the Minnesota Department of Health and coordinator of the Minnesota Public Health Collaborative for Quality Improvement, in developing this chapter.
2. Mobilizing for Action through Planning and Partnerships (MAPP), http://www.naccho.org/topics/infrastructure/MAPP/index.cfm (accessed July 12, 2009). MAPP is a community-driven strategic planning tool for improving community health.
3. Turning Point: From Silos to Systems, http://www.phf.org/pmqi/silossystems.pdf. Public Health Foundation (accessed June 5, 2009). Turning point is a strategic model for the use of performance standards, measures, progress reports, and ongoing quality improvement efforts to ensure a public health agency achieves desired results.
4. Baldrige National Quality Program, Criteria for Performance Excellence, 2009–2010, http://www.baldrige.nist.gov (accessed July 5, 2009).
5. R. Bialek, G. Duffy, and J. Moran, eds., *The Public Health Quality Improvement Handbook,* (Milwaukee, WI: Quality Press, 2009): 15.
6. Coalition Sub-Group Members: L. Beitsch, R. Bialek, A. Cofsky, L. Corso, J. Moran, W. Riley, and P. Russo.
7. W. Riley, J. W. Moran, L. Corso, L. Beitsch, R. Bialek, and A. Cofsky, "Defining Quality Improvement in Public Health." *Journal of Public Health Management and Practice,* Lippincott Williams & Wilkins, Philadelphia, PA, (2009).
8. G. J. Langley, K. M. Nolan, T. W. Nolan, C. L. Norman, and L. P. Provost, "The Improvement Guide: A Practical Approach to Enhancing Organizational Performance," 2nd ed. (San Francisco: Jossey-Bass, 2009).
9. D. Thingstad-Boe, W. Riley, and H. Parsons, "Improving Service Delivery in a County Health Department WIC Clinic: An Application of Statistical Process Control Techniques," *American Journal of Public Health,* no. 9 (2009): 1619–1625.
10. U.S. Department of Agriculture, Food and Nutrition Service, "About WIC." Retrieved July 8, 2009, at http://www.fns.usda.gov/wic/
11. W. Riley and K. McCoy, "QI Collaboratives for a Healthier Minnesota," *World Conference on Quality and Improvement* (Session W06, Minneapolis, 2009).
12. M. L. Woelfel, R. Abusabha, R. Pruzek, H. Stratton, G. Chen, and L. S. Edmunds, "Barrier to the Use of WIC Services," *Journal of American Diet Association,* 104 (2004): 736–743.
13. C. G. Green, M. Harison, K. Henderson, and A. Lenihan, "A Total Quality Management in the Delivery of Public Health Services: A Focus on North Carolina WIC Programs," *Journal of Public Health Management Practices*, 4, 72 (1998): 81.
14. Thingstad-Boe, Riley, and Parsons, p. 9.
15. W. Riley and K. McCoy, "QI Collaboratives for a Healthier Minnesota," *World Conference on Quality and Improvement* (Session W06, Minneapolis, 2009).
16. http://www.health.state.mn.us/divs/cfh/ophp/system/schsac/ (accessed July 12, 2009).
17. http://www.health.state.mn.us/divs/cfh/ophp/system/schsac/ (accessed July 12, 2009).

18. http://www.health.state.mn.us/ppmrs/ (accessed July 12, 2009).
19. National Network of Public Health Institutes, http://www.nnphi.org/mlc (accessed July 13, 2009), New Orleans, LA.
20. Public Health Accreditation Board, http://www.phaboard.org/ (accessed July 13, 2009), Alexandria, VA.
21. Langley, Nolan, Nolan, Norman, and Provost, "The Improvement Guide: A Practical Approach to Enhancing Organizational Performance."
22. R. Bialek, G. L. Duffy, and J. W. Moran, "Daily Management," *The Public Health Quality Improvement Handbook* (Milwaukee, WI: ASQ Quality Press, 2009), pp. 1–14.
23. J. B. ReVelle, J. W. Moran, and C. A. Cox, *The QFD Handbook* (New York: John Wiley & Sons, 1998).
24. M. L. George, *Lean Six Sigma for Service* (New York: McGraw Hill, 2003).
25. W. Riley, H. Parsons, K. McCoy, D. Burns, D. Anderson, S. Lee, and F. Sainfort, "Introducing Quality Improvement Methods into Local Public Health Departments: Structured Evaluation of a Statewide Pilot Project," *Public Health Services and Systems Researcher,* 44, no. 5 (October 2009, part II).

# 2

# Introduction to Quality Function Deployment[1] and Lean-Six Sigma

## INTRODUCTION TO QUALITY FUNCTION DEPLOYMENT

Quality function deployment is a system for translating customer requirements into appropriate features at each stage of the development of a concept, to the definition of the function to produce it, to designing the delivery process, and finally to defining the marketing campaign to inform the potential customer of its availability and readiness for use.

Quality function deployment (QFD) had its foundation in the requirements interface matrix[2] (RIM), which was developed by the Ramo Wooldridge Corporation in the 1950s. The requirements interface matrix was used to ensure a rational process of how an organization produces services based on the needs and expectations of the customer. The RIM was later expanded by the Japanese in their development of QFD.

QFD was developed from the Japanese expression *Hin Shitsu, Ki No, Ten Kai*. There are many meanings to each of these words. *Hin Shitsu* can mean quality, features, attributes, or qualities. *Ki No* can mean functions or mechanisms. *Ten Kai* can mean deployment, evolution, diffusion, or development. QFD was adopted as the terminology to integrate these multiple meanings. The initials QFD have become known as follows:

- Q—quality of your output—how well it meets and satisfies your customer's requirements

- F—the function is what defines the size, shape, or form of your output—what you do or produce

- D—how you do it, the deployment—how the process is aligned to customer needs and wants

The QFD process was developed by Y. Akao and T. Fukuhara. Each developed a similar but different approach. Akao's approach is based on a matrix of 30 matrices.[3] Fukuhara's approach was based on four matrices.[4] In 1995 J. ReVelle and J. Moran[5] developed six additional matrices to help in preparing, managing, and reviewing QFD projects.

The main purpose of QFD is to ensure that the voice of the customer (VOC) is fully understood and incorporated throughout the design and development process of a product or service. The VOC consists of how a process should perform as defined by the customer. QFD helps an organization understand how well it satisfies its current customers and what future customer needs and wants will be for new products or services.

QFD has a built-in competitive benchmarking process that helps an organization focus on how much it may need to improve to not only meet the customer's expressed needs, but also to exceed the competitor's strengths. Public Health agencies may feel that they have no competitors for their services and programs. This type of thinking usually leads to the "captive customer" approach regarding the development of a product or service. The captive customer approach can apply to both the organization's internal and external customers. Because the internal and external captive customer voice is never captured, these customers usually receive a product or service that they have to take or leave. If they take it, the internal customers wind up with a process that is difficult to use and implement, while the external customers find using the program difficult and sometimes impossible. Sometimes the process designers are amazed at the complaints heard from captive customers and wonder why they are not appreciative of the product or service they finally receive. This explains why public assistance programs are often overly complex; where those delivering the services do not fully understand the process or clients who need the service do not obtain it.

Competitive benchmarking should not be ignored for Public Health programs. It is important to find a similar type of delivery of a service or product from other sectors (profit, service, and nonprofit) to benchmark or use national or state health benchmarks. The purpose of benchmarking is to learn from others where an organization should think about making improvements. One of the benefits the authors have found about QFD is that it forces organizations to look outside of their comfort zone and learn from other sectors that may be doing extraordinary things to satisfy their customers. These extraordinary things may stimulate out-of-the-box thinking, which may help translate customer delights from another sector into the development of Public Health product or services.

The QFD process is a team-based process that is a structured and disciplined approach to product and service design, redesign, and development. The QFD team in Public Health must include service providers, support staff, community representatives, and the customer (the direct recipient and the final recipient).

The direct recipient is the client who receives the benefit from the Public Health agency, and the final recipient is the community where a client resides.

QFD supports an organization's quality improvement initiatives by:

- Developing an objective definition of product and service quality to be achieved

- Teaching the organization about the value of capturing and deploying the voice of the customer throughout the organization

- Providing products and services that satisfy internal and external customers

- Training participants in a tool and technique that can be used in other teaming activities

- Strengthening the teaming process

- Helping develop an organization-wide deployment process based on the VOC

QFD has an important benefit in that it becomes a product or service project's memory. Through the use of the QFD matrices, the decisions (interrelationships) of the QFD team are captured and deployed. The matrices become a central repository that can be used to update management of new team members and develop new matrices. The QFD matrices approach allows for the transfer of information and knowledge in a compact form that does not require pages of written text to document.

These matrices take traditional QFD into the realm of the delivery process; the original QFD tool focused solely on function and concept. The foundation of an effective QFD activity is the perfect springboard into product and service delivery, including measures and targets to monitor ongoing performance. In Public Health, this means it is not adequate to just plan for being client and community oriented, but also that the programs and services must meet the quality goals as perceived by the client with measurements to ensure that the goals are actually met.

QFD provides a process to help standardize the health department's internal language and reduce semantic debates between functional team representatives. The time saved on semantic debates can be put to better use, such as focusing on developing a common vision of a Public Health program design to ensure it is truly customer focused. The QFD process helps the team members turn their individual reactions, emotions, convictions, and thoughts into focused actions. This helps the team overcome their interpersonal difficulties, frees their creativity, and increases the team's motivation. Reducing interpersonal difficulties increases the trust, honesty, and cooperation in the team.

QFD is a highly systematic and disciplined process that requires management's active involvement and support. QFD is not a spectator sport but one that requires active management involvement. This is not a process that can be delegated by the decision makers. Each matrix interaction builds on the next one and so on. Decision makers need to make these decisions and not second guess them at a later date. The decision makers have to be actively involved in all aspects of a QFD study and its review for maximum results.

## INTRODUCTION TO LEAN-SIX SIGMA

The techniques of Lean-Six Sigma are a natural partner to the application of QFD. Lean-Six Sigma is a methodology that integrates concepts and tools from lean operations and Six Sigma methodologies. The concept of *lean* evolved from a series of quality and performance improvement models dating back to the work of W. Edwards Deming and Joseph A. Juran in the 1950s. Deming and Juran concluded that organizations must eliminate waste and reduce time to market in order for services and products to remain competitive. Unless all resources are directly engaged in the fulfillment of a customer need, something is being wasted. There will always be a competitor who can do the same function for less, or faster, or better given the same use of resources.

*Six Sigma* is a continuous process improvement methodology that facilitates near perfection in the processes of an organization. It considers not only the average performance but also the variability of what a health department presents to the community. This variation is often the cause of what is considered the penalty for not getting it right the first time. In terms of Public Health activities, it consists of rework costs to reprocess forms before delivery to the client, scrap costs, recovery from a bad client experience, and concessions for late service or paperwork deliveries, just to name a few.

Lean addresses reduction of waste and cycle time, while Six Sigma focuses on customer acceptance. A useful way to distinguish between the two sides of Lean-Six Sigma is to think of the profit equation most familiar to the business community:

$$\text{Revenues} - \text{Expenses} = \text{Profit}$$

In the Public Health community, this equation might be better represented as:

$$\text{Funding} - \text{Expenses} = \text{Available Capital}$$

Available capital in a Public Health setting means resources that can be devoted to programs or administrative functions required to deliver products and services. The authors have observed innovative Public Health departments increasing the amount of cash available for priority programs in two ways: reducing the money spent to provide a service and increasing the ability of the department to bring in additional resources to fund operations.

Eliminating errors and reducing redundant functions saves money from being spent in the first place. Rarely is a Public Health worker lost for things to do. When we are doing the right things in the right way, every bit of salary and administrative support expenses are targeted toward the highest priority outcomes for the department and the community. That is the lean approach.

Increasing the ability to bring in cash comes from improved reputation of the department and increased ability to write winning grant applications. When the local health department strengthens the relationship with its Board of Advisors, charitable contributors, grant funding bodies, and government sources, it becomes easier to compete for awards. Six Sigma addresses the customer-focused side of Lean-Six Sigma by ensuring a reliable and continuously improving performance record for the department. Reducing variation against all critical targets of the organization means the department always has a great story to tell the media, the community, and the many stakeholders, who provide funding for operations. Sustainable processes within the department allow grant writers a firm foundation from which to identify attainable outcomes, target populations, and operational results.

Lean concepts go beyond the traditional manufacturing shop floor and are applicable to Public Health departments. Companies have realized great benefit by implementing lean techniques in the office functions of manufacturing firms, as well as in purely service firms such as banks, Public Health departments, restaurants, and retail establishments. Public Health departments (PHDs) are becoming aware of the benefits of a lean approach through collaborative projects with corporate and government community partners and through peer communications at conferences and meetings around the United States.

A definition of lean, used by the Manufacturing Extension Partnership (of NIST/MEP, a part of the U.S. Department of Commerce) is "Lean establishes a systematic approach to eliminating wastes and creating flow throughout the whole company."[6] Lean focuses on value-added expenditure of resources from the customers' viewpoint. Another way of putting it would be to give the clients and community:

- What they want

- When they want it

- Where they want it

- In the quantities and varieties they want.

A planned, systematic implementation of lean leads to improved quality, more resources, increased reputation and demand, greater productivity and throughput, and improved morale.

The concepts and tools of lean and Six Sigma complement each other strongly in the operational environment. Lean enterprise applications address the short-term requirements of reducing waste, effectively balancing resources, and improving productivity within the operating unit. Six Sigma provides strong overlapping tools and methodologies, including new technologies, while bringing in additional approaches for client-focused orientation and opportunities for increasing the organization's reputation within both the local and the wider communities. The authors have observed that the concept of lean, by eliminating waste and duplication in existing processes, appears to be the best first step in using the tools of Lean-Six Sigma for long term organizational performance success.

Figure 2.1 compares high-level activity steps for lean and two of the Six Sigma approaches most often discussed in business literature.[7] The lean flow begins with analyzing existing systems, whether performing as designed or needing improvement. Subsequent steps guide the improvement team to identify priority areas for reducing waste, eliminating defects, and improving performance. The full lean flow of analyze, plan, focus, deliver, and improve assumes an existing process that is documented sufficiently to study through process observation and resulting data analysis.

The middle flow in Figure 2.1 is of the continuous process improvement version of Six Sigma, DMAIC. This technique was developed to reduce variation

**Lean Six Sigma incorporates, and deploys, the key methods, tools, and techniques of its predecessors.**

*Lean focuses on waste elimination in existing processes.*

*Six Sigma focuses on Continuous Process Improvement (DMAIC) to reduce variation in existing processes.*

*Six Sigma also focuses on New Process Design/Complete Redesign (DMEDI) for wholesale redesign of processes as well as new products and services.*

Source: Byrne, George, Lubowe, Dave, and Blitz, Amy, Driving Operational Innovation Using Lean Six Sigma, IBM Global Business Services, 2007.

**Figure 2.1**  Process flow comparisons of predecessor methodologies.

in existing processes. Once a process is stable and functioning as designed to meet customer requirements, the goal is to reduce as much variation as possible to provide a repeatable platform for planning and estimating return on investment (ROI) for subsequent performance of the targeted process. The steps in the DMAIC process—define, measure, analyze, improve, and control—like lean, assume an existing, documented process.

The third flow in Figure 2.1 focuses on new process design or complete redesign of existing processes. These processes may be for redesign of operations related to existing programs or design of new services delivered to clients and the community. As in the DMAIC flow, this redesign flow begins with define. Like the continuous improvement or problem-solving sequences identified by Joseph Juran in the 1950s, this flow realizes the importance of defining the current state. The next step, measure, provides the quantitative data of both the current and potential future states to allow decisions concerning possible solutions for radical redesign of a process, product, or service. The final three steps—explore, develop, and implement—provide the structure by which the agreed-upon solution becomes a tangible process, product, or service to be tested and hopefully made available to a delighted customer market.

Where lean seeks to reduce all waste from a designed process (efficiency) on the operations side, Six Sigma reduces variation in the process (effectiveness) for maximum acceptance by the client. Lean-Six Sigma is a robust set of tools and techniques with which to assess the output of the initial voice of the customer as gathered by the QFD function. As the QFD process drills down into technical design requirements for program or service design, additional lean and Six Sigma tools provide the structure by which effective data-gathering and decision-making drive toward ultimate end user, client, and stakeholder satisfaction.

## SUMMARY

QFD provides an approach to prioritize, organize, focus, direct, and measure how well a QI team has integrated the voice of the customer into its proposed solution. Lean-Six Sigma provides a means to maximize shareholder value, but because Public Health does not have shareholders we substitute stakeholders as those who need Public Health programs and services. Lean-Six Sigma will supplement QFD by helping achieve for stakeholders the fastest rate of improvement in customer satisfaction, cost, quality, process speed, and invested dollars. The fusion of QFD and Lean-Six Sigma will provide a methodology and tools to ensure that the stakeholders receive products and services they need and desire delivered by a defect-free designed process that is the fastest and most predictable and efficient possible.

# ENDNOTES

1. The material in this chapter was adopted from "Introduction to Quality Function Deployment: Lecture Notes," J. Moran (1995).
2. Air Force System Command Manual, 375-1 (1952), and S. B. Johnson, "Three Approaches to Big Technology: Operations Research, Systems Engineering, and Project Management," *Society for the History of Technology* (1997).
3. J. ReVelle, J. Moran, and C. Cox, *The QFD Handbook* (New York: John Wiley & Sons, 1998), 57.
4. ReVelle, Moran, and Cox, *The QFD Handbook,* 56.
5. J. Moran and J. ReVelle, *The Executive's Handbook on Quality Function Deployment,* (Markon, 1994), 5–35; and ReVelle, Moran, and Cox, *The QFD Handbook,* 267–291.
6. http://www.mep.nist.gov/manufacturers/services/lean/index.htm (accessed May 28, 2009).
7. G. Byrne, D. Lubowe, and A. Blitz, "Driving Operational Innovation Using Lean Six Sigma," *IBM Global Business Services,* 2007, http://www-931.ibm.com/tela/webmail/Newsletter/6749/19191 (accessed May, 2009).

# 3

# An Integrated QI Approach: QFD and LSS Support Macro, Meso, Micro

## INTRODUCTION

Using the voice of the customer (VOC) at each step of the process to fulfill client requirements is an effective way to meet community health needs. Chapter 1, "The Continuum of Quality Improvement in Public Health," introduces a systems approach to quality improvement (QI). Meeting health department client and stakeholder requirements is the intent of QI within Public Health. The goal is to achieve ever more effective delivery of programs and services for a healthy community population. QFD assists in capturing the VOC and translating it into programs and service features that satisfy the client, the community, and other interested parties.

Figure 3.1 illustrates a high-level sequence of steps for translating the VOC into effective community health programs and services. QFD activities, beginning with the Macro phase of gathering the VOC, map client requirements to health department functions through product/service planning. Fulfilling client needs and requirements is assigned during the Meso phase to a unit within the health department. Functional managers design the program or project using requirements from authorized local, state, federal, or funding bodies.

The Meso phase ends with the identification of processes developed by frontline supervisors and staff. Additional QFD activities guide the function design and provide a direct link back to initial VOC input. The Micro phase begins with the operational definition of key processes and design for delivering the services to individuals and the community. As introduced in Chapter 2, "Introduction to Quality Function Deployment and Lean-Six Sigma," lean principles guide teams and individuals in the development of effective and efficient procedures. Some of the lean principles are listed in Figure 3.1. More of these principles are discussed in later chapters.

Establishing controls for monitoring process performance and service results is the final step in the Micro phase. This activity is critical for maintaining

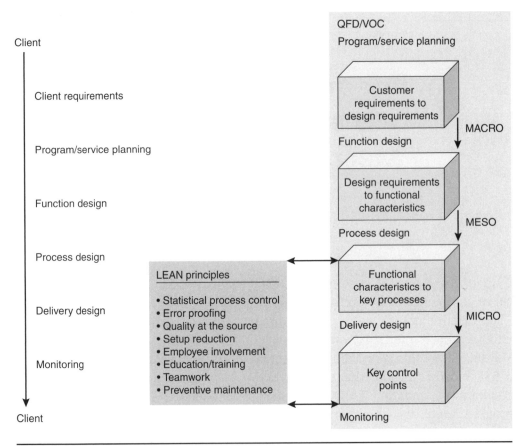

**Figure 3.1**   The QFD/VOC integrated fulfillment approach.

the effectiveness of the new program or service. Measures such as those recommended by the turning point model (Chapter 1) are a useful starting point. The ongoing monitoring through internal or external audits provides feedback to ensure that the service reaching the client is what the VOC originally identified. Chapter 7, "Milestones and Measures," offers additional techniques for monitoring interim and final results of health department activities.

The tools of Lean-Six Sigma are used in a number of service industries to design services that effectively meet customer needs. *Six Sigma* tools measure and monitor for improvement opportunities, while *lean* tools help design systems to reduce errors and eliminate waste. Three chapters in this book expand on the concepts of Lean-Six Sigma (LSS): Chapter 5, "Process Analysis and Waste Reduction," details the basic premise of designing services for maximum effectiveness with minimum resource commitment, while Chapter 8, "Lean-Six Sigma: Faster Better Smarter," and Chapter 9, "The House of Lean-Six Sigma Tools and Techniques," relate the core concepts of lean and Six Sigma to the functions of Public Health.

# INTEGRATED PROCESSES CREATE A SYSTEM

The performance of a health department depends mostly on execution of the department's core processes. Execution effectiveness and the efficiency of each core process depend in turn on process organization, resources, and capabilities. Executing plans in the most effective way possible is the responsibility of Public Health leaders. In Public Health, current efforts for achieving accreditation based on a common set of essential services are defining standard performance expectations for health departments. Over time, a database of performance indicators will allow health department leadership to compare local performance against the combined performance across health departments at the national level. We are in competition with ourselves to provide increasingly better services and products to our respective communities.

Department leaders can obtain better results when core processes are implemented differently and in a better way. Leaders execute core processes differently because their processes are better organized, are performed on a more effective and efficient resource platform, and are powered by better capabilities.

The general model of process-based organization performance, presented in Figure 3.2, was conceived as an attempt to help leaders execute core processes

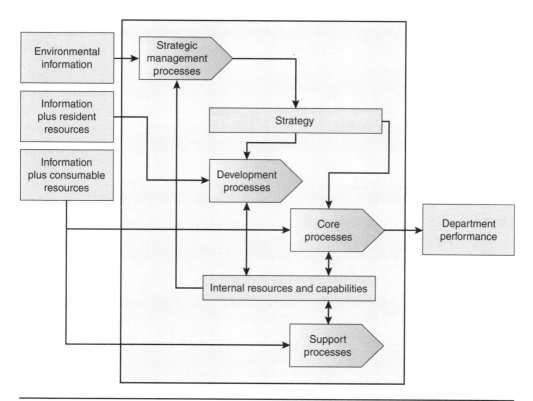

**Figure 3.2**    General model of process-based health department performance.

better. It also puts into a comprehensive context all the key success factors behind sustained department performance.

Within the model, four processes and activities are separated:

1. Strategic management processes

2. Development processes

3. Core processes

4. Support processes[1]

Department leadership uses information from community assessments and other environmental scans to identify information and resource needs for the next operating period; usually the fiscal year. Figure 3.2 labels these needs as resident (fixed) resources, and consumable (variable) resources.

Strategic management processes create the department strategy using external information based on client and community needs, as well as local, state, and national health trends. Internal information on existing resources and capabilities, as well as the existing strategy, is also taken into account. The new strategy guides development processes that are invoked for implementation of core and support processes. Development processes design and develop new products or services; they also build new resident resources and modify or reconfigure existing ones. This includes tangible resources such as buildings and technology, as well as intangible resources such as organizational structure, management systems, and workforce capacity. Finally, development processes build new or modify existing operational capabilities.

Resident resources enable the execution of core processes that convert information flows and consumable resources into community client services. Support processes (such as human resources and information technology) keep alive core processes (such as a WIC program or community education department). Support processes maintain the status quo of resources and capabilities.

Strategy execution is the biggest impact on department performance and consists of the continuous execution of the core and support processes. Once strategy is set and processes are implemented, operational excellence behind well-designed core processes delivers desired services to the client and the community. Continuous improvement, monitoring, and maintenance make department performance sustainable. Superior department performance depends on development processes and a sound, realistic strategy, based on a deep understanding of client needs.

Strategic processes are the ones needed to manage the department's long-term vision. They include processes and activities such as:

• Define mission, vision, and strategy

• Develop strategic plans at the department and functional unit level

- Develop plans for execution of strategic initiatives

- Monitor execution of strategic plans and initiatives

*Strategic management processes* provide the abilities to assess the environment; to assess the internal operations of the department, to define strategic choices on where to provide services and how; and, finally, to make the right decision on strategic direction. Strategy is the most important success factor for long-term superior department performance. The impact of strategic management processes on department performance is mostly indirect, however.

These strategic processes increase value creation in the future. They are considered a support process (rather than core process) and generate cost rather than produce a service.

*Development processes* implement the new strategy. They also enable the department to adapt in response to its environment. Development processes build something new inside the department, or change on a large scale whatever is already going on. This development applies to resident resources in particular, whether tangible or intangible, or operational capabilities.

Development processes are used whenever a new strategy is defined, and they inevitably call for changes in the resource base. They are also invoked whenever feedback on department performance indicates that there is something wrong with the existing program or service delivery of core processes or underlying resources.

As is the case with strategic processes, development processes are a support process cost to the health department. Because of their strategic nature, they can reduce the value created for the department in the current operating period and the impact on short-run performance can be negative due to costs for personnel time and administrative activity. These processes, however, offer the promise of increased value creation in the future and thus justify investment in the judgment of senior decision makers.

*Core activities* create current value for the health department because they are involved in the creation of current community programs and client services. Without core activities, the health department would not deliver client services or community programs. In a manufacturing company, core activities are involved in the transformation of inputs into outputs delivered to its customers inside the company. Some core activities, such as *Create Purchase Orders,* deal with a department's material inputs and aim at reducing costs. Other core activities, such as *Perform Routine Process Audits* or *Conduct Community Assessment,* convert input flows into output flows; that is, they identify operational requirements and thus generate most of the value for our clients within the community. The remaining core activities, such as *Enter and Validate Client Service Record,* capture value for the department to realize cash recovery from the outputs of service activities. In a service company, core activities rely mostly on interactions with customers, on handling their requests and on related information processing. For example, in a bank, such activities as *Open Account for a New Customer, Check Customer Credibility, Issue Checkbook,* and *Distribute Account Statements* are performed.

In a health department one set of Environmental Health core activities might be *Open Application for New Septic System, Receive Payment from Contractor, Perform Site Evaluation, Perform Application Review, Approve Application,* and *Inform Contractor.* Activities developed to support core processes are what keep the department in business. Core processes create outputs that clients, funding bodies, and the community value. Core processes bring in the resources needed to produce the services.

Some core processes do not directly bring in funding. They are background tasks performed to keep the department running. Background activities are necessary to run the health department but do not contribute directly to client value creation. Instead, they enable execution and continuous performance of other activities. Some background activities support the department as a whole and focus on its infrastructure and common resources, while others are associated with specific clusters of core activities. Examples of such background activities are the following:

- Hire a new employee

- Provide IT helpdesk support

- Install security access on immunology/STD office door

- Maintain chart of accounts

- Post accounting transactions

Another group of background activities includes ones directed at the creation of value for the department in the future and thus are crucial to its long-term survival and growth. Their costs are absorbed in the present to preserve or increase value creation in the future. This category is exemplified by activities required for designing and developing new products or services, or activities required for developing the department's strategy and ensuring its successful implementation. Examples of such background activities are:

- Perform community assessment

- Generate grant proposals

- Document current service specifications

- Establish an integrated quality system

- Develop strategic initiatives for enhanced community partnerships

*Support processes* are the least glamorous of department processes. They are needed primarily to feed the strategy execution function. They keep the infrastructure going so the health department can perform the core processes that meet client needs and improve community health metrics. Some examples of support processes are:

- Lobby reception desk support

- Housekeeping services

- Motor pool operations

- Security monitoring

Support processes are generally routine and continuously run in the background. As in the case of other background processes, support processes generate only costs. They are, however, indispensable and must be performed to keep the doors of departments and clinics open. Some of them improve or extend services that the department already performs. Such capabilities would be used to quickly adjust or improve selected activities, or redesign a group of related activities.

## THE HUMAN INTERACTION WITH MACRO, MESO, AND MICRO LEVELS: INDIVIDUAL QI

All activities of the department are part of a total system designed expressly to meet client and community needs. In a perfect world, no health department resource would be expended unless it directly contributes to providing service to a client. Unfortunately, indirect functions, such as background activities and support processes, still must be performed to provide the foundation for direct client services.

An integrated approach to technology, infrastructure, and personnel helps envision the interaction required among human and system to maximize department performance. Figure 3.3 illustrates that not only technical systems, organizational structures, and processes—but also the mindsets of employees—can affect the department's ability to meet the goals it set during strategic planning.[2]

This chapter has already discussed the planning and delivery of client services. Quality systems such as quality function deployment and Lean-Six Sigma provide tools for designing error-free processes and reducing waste and variation. Support and background activities also call for efficient labor allocation and the ongoing function of maintenance systems, as identified under technical systems in Figure 3.3.

Management infrastructure ties the technical system to the human system through design of performance and talent management processes. Organizational

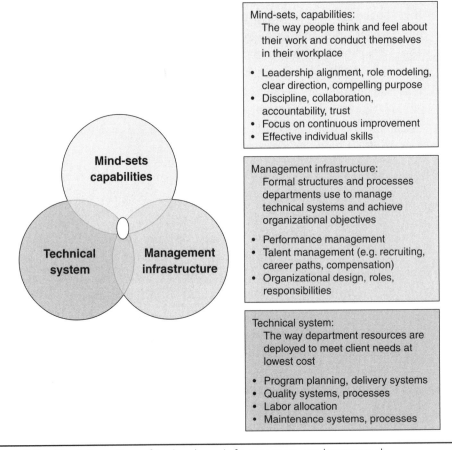

Mind-sets, capabilities:
  The way people think and feel about their work and conduct themselves in their workplace

- Leadership alignment, role modeling, clear direction, compelling purpose
- Discipline, collaboration, accountability, trust
- Focus on continuous improvement
- Effective individual skills

Management infrastructure:
  Formal structures and processes departments use to manage technical systems and achieve organizational objectives

- Performance management
- Talent management (e.g. recruiting, career paths, compensation)
- Organizational design, roles, responsibilities

Technical system:
  The way department resources are deployed to meet client needs at lowest cost

- Program planning, delivery systems
- Quality systems, processes
- Labor allocation
- Maintenance systems, processes

**Figure 3.3**   The integration of technology, infrastructure, and personnel.

designs, such as job descriptions, reporting structures, standards of performance, roles, and responsibilities identify expected behaviors within the department.

Equally critical to the effective performance of the health department is the mind-set or attitude of the employee community. Aligning leadership vision, mission, and values to each program is essential. Providing clear direction and purpose is a direct outcome of the strategic management process. Leadership mind-set and role modeling includes discipline, collaboration, accountability, and trust. The leadership mind-set is the foundation for a total culture of continuous improvement within the health department focused on both internal and external customer requirements. Finally, the culture of continuous improvement is maintained in the long term by creation of a learning environment in which employees are empowered to upgrade their individual skills based on the needs of their work assignments.

The process groups introduced in Figure 3.2—strategic management, development, core, and support—do not happen by themselves. They are designed by personnel within the health department, or obtained by sharing process designs with other organizations. The integration of technology, management infrastructure, and employee mindset create the culture for effective department performance. Figure 3.4 maps the role of health department personnel in implementing the Macro, Meso, Micro, and Individual activities of QI.

The VOC and other community assessment vehicles provide senior leadership with critical requirements for client services. Senior management identifies the vision and overall goals of the health department through strategic planning activities. Senior leadership then partners with functional managers based on their role as leaders of individual programs or units within the department to establish annual goals. The functional managers elicit the assistance of first-line supervisors and team leaders to break objectives down into operational tasks to be performed by the front-line workforce.

Arrows in Figure 3.4 show policy deployed downward from senior leadership at the Macro level, through the Meso level of the functional manager to the workforce at the Micro level, while tasks, measures, and completion dates or milestones are communicated upward. The workforce at the Micro/Individual level also receives the voice of the customer through face-to-face communication with the client, thus providing a feedback loop for validation of the strategy.

The feedback loop of validating the VOC at both ends of department activities provides a never-ending system of QI and sustainability. QFD, supported by the methods and tools of Lean-Six Sigma, effectively integrates the VOC into the

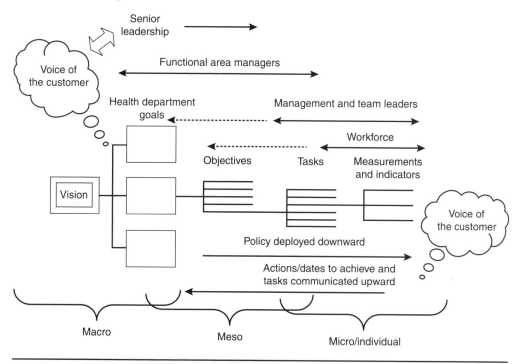

**Figure 3.4**   The mechanics of an integrated approach to QI.

fabric of department operations with every project undertaken. Little by little, employees, managers, and leaders will learn the methods and tools of QI. Little by little, the department will shift to a more robust way of measuring and delivering quality on-time and under budget . . . which will delight clients, which will delight shareholders, which will deliver value to the community.

## ENDNOTES

1. G. Grzegorz, "The Process-Based View of a Company—Principles and Applications, Part 3," *BPTrends* (March 2009).
2. D. Fine, M. A. Hansen, and S. Roggenhoffer, "From Lean to Lasting: Making Operational Improvements Stick," *The McKinsey Quarterly* (November 2008).

# 4

# Customer Focus: Revitalizing Your Organization to Become Customer Centric

There are many definitions of quality, but in the final analysis quality is defined by the customer or end user based upon customer experience with the health department's programs and services. The customer compares a service or program with his or her own expectations of that experience and then assesses the difference between reality and perception.[1] The customer experience is the aggregate of all the *touch points* that customers and stakeholders have with the health department processes that deliver your programs and services.

Figure 4.1 shows a client relationship model that identifies the various elements that must be considered when assessing the needs of a client or stakeholder and to build a continual relationship commitment from them. As in any marketing or needs assessment study, it is important to identify primary customers and stakeholders. In public health these may be clients, other persons served, community partners, funding bodies, and additional stakeholders involved in serving the health needs of the public. Identifying and segmenting clients and stakeholders into subsets allows the local health department (LHD) to prioritize the activities dedicated to a particular client or stakeholder set. Different client and stakeholder sets have different profiles and require different interactions and outcomes as they relate to the programs of the health department. Once the profiles are identified and differentiated, these different requirements can be integrated into the daily operations of the LHD in a way that most effectively meets the needs of the external customers (client and community) as well as those within the health department itself.

Differentiating the profiles of customer sets allows a more effective focus on the needs assessment for each client community population. Once those needs are assessed, the organization begins the process of identifying objectives and goals based on the Five Ps:

1. *Planning:* What is the best way to involve this customer set in satisfying their particular needs?

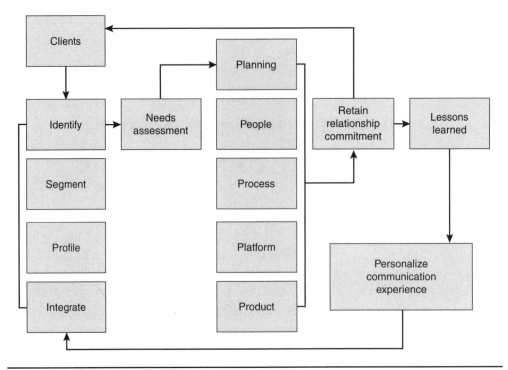

**Figure 4.1** Client relationship model.

2. *People:* What are the behavioral and psychological needs of this customer set?

3. *Process:* What LHD processes are targeted to the needs of this customer? What modifications are necessary to better meet customer needs?

4. *Platform:* Is the LHD structured appropriately to meet the needs of this customer set? Are the LHD's policies and procedures robust enough to meet this set of customer requirements?

5. *Program:* Finally, are the programs and services currently offered by the LHD adequate to meet the needs of this customer set now and in the future?

Working through the Five Ps of the client relationship model is an iterative process. Feedback continually exchanged between the LHD and the person or population served helps balance needs and offerings. Models such as mobilizing for action through planning and partnerships (MAPP), the 10 essential services, accreditation, and turning point are excellent tools for reviewing community needs and the LHD's ability to serve its communities.

This continual interchange creates a commitment to the relationship on both sides, customer and LHD. As the relationship continues, successes and missed targets provide valuable lessons learned that are fed back into the planning cycle for improved communication among the health department, clients, and community. Over time, the relationship becomes truly personal through trust, transparency, and sharing. In the long term, this personalized relationship provides the foundation upon which new customer profiles, segmentation, and strong partnerships are forged.

A flowchart of the entire service process helps us understand the experiences of a client or community when they come into contact with the health department. Then you will be able to identify the touch points and ask, "What does your customer . . ."

- See? (Initial reaction?)
- Feel?
- Hear?
- Smell?
- Sense?
- Experience?

The answers (by both internal and external customers) provide a starting point in understanding what might be your organization's current level of customer satisfaction. It also gives some general improvement direction as management starts to design or redesign a program or service.

Figure 4.2 shows a matrix that can be used, once a process has been flowcharted, to help you understand which of the process steps touch your internal and external customers. For example, the matrix helps you understand which of the processes are customer touch points, the performance of the touch point in delivering customer satisfaction, and which data are needed from the customer at that particular touch point. It will be shown in Chapters 12 and 13 how quality function deployment (QFD) is used to analyze customer needs through a series of matrices (matrices make the presentation of complex concepts much simpler).

Too often organizations lack customer focus, as they were built over many years through culture and leadership actions. The customer culture may be one in which the customer is the central focus or just an afterthought. In Public Health it is possible to develop a *captive customer* attitude because clients and communities must take what is given if no alternative programs or services are available. Although uncommon in Public Health, it is apparent in some government agencies that those providing service are uncaring about the service level provided.[2] Such an attitude and demeanor (see and hear) suggest that clients are an inconvenience and an interruption to the agency's routine.

| Customer needs → | Internal customers | | | External customers | | | Total ✓s | Current performance | What data could we capture? |
|---|---|---|---|---|---|---|---|---|---|
| | A | B | C | X | Y | Z | | | |
| Process flow steps / Touch points | | ✓ | | | | | | | |
| | | | ✓ | ✓ | | | | | |
| | ✓ | | | | | ✓ | | | |
| | | | | ✓ | | | | | |
| Current satisfaction met (M) or unmet (U) | | | | | | | | | |
| Improvement opportunity? Y/N? | | | | | | | | | |

**Figure 4.2**   Which process steps impact customer needs?

If an organization lacks customer focus, it is a good idea to investigate the root cause of why that attitude persists. A cause and effect diagram, such as the one shown in Figure 4.3, helps capture all the potential causes of a lack of customer focus and is a good tool with which to start the analysis.

The cause and effect diagram shows that poor customer service, on the far right, is the effect. Numerous causes are identified, including poor staff training, inadequate resources, and lack of leadership commitment.

An organization that lacks customer focus often has not identified its customer or does not know what the customer wants and needs. "Who is the customer?" is the first question to ask when analyzing a health department program or service. To answer the question, the manager needs to understand the *function* and the process that produces a value-added output. A function is the result of the inputs that are combined to produce an output of value to a customer. The function should be something a customer (internal or external) wants and needs. Sometimes a function is best understood by a description of its properties:

- Inputs

- Process steps that convert inputs

- Outputs

- Capability of process over time

- Speed of operation

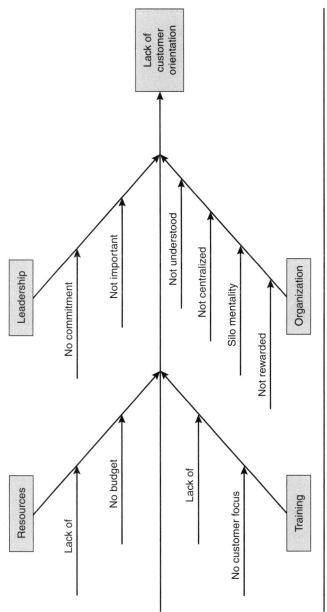

**Figure 4.3**  Cause and effect diagram of poor customer service.

Once the properties of the function are understood, the next step is to focus on how the function relates to the rest of the health department's functions.

- What is the function's relationship to other functions?

- Is the process a subfunction of another process?

- How does the function combine with other functions?

- Is the output another function's input?

- Do I understand how the function contributes to the health department's overall success?

- If I change a process within the function, how will the change influence the health department as a whole?

Once the function is completely understood, the next step is to identify customers for the function and then classify them into a number of categories:

- Internal customer (within the department)

- External customer (client or community that receives a service)

- Primary customer (?)

- Secondary customer (?)

- Ultimate purchaser (governmental source, grant, user fees)

When there is a clear understanding of the customer category, the next step is to develop a process to obtain the voice of the customer (VOC). The VOC consists of what the customer expects from the health department. This requires the health department to design and develop a methodology that will, on a regular basis, track and record the wants and needs of the customer base and any changes in needs. This can be accomplished through the use of surveys, telephone interviews, person-to-person questionnaires at the touch points in the process, and outside firms. A health department must have one or more of these methods to capture its voice of the customer in a regular and timely manner since its purpose is based on client and community satisfaction.

Obtaining the voice of the customer requires an understanding of four factors shown in Figure 4.4:

- How to define the customer (categorize the customer)

- How to hear the customer's voice (routinely track the customer's needs)

- How to evaluate the customer's voice (analyze and interpret the customer's needs)

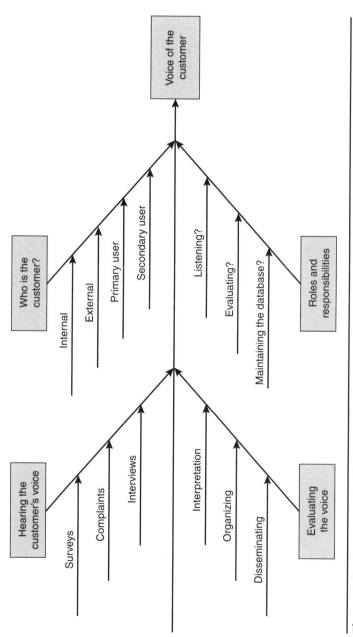

**Figure 4.4**  Factors to obtain the VOC.

- How to define the roles for achieving the above items (assign the responsibility to a specific person or program)

When obtaining the voice of the customer, it is important to understand the customer's:

- Wants

- Needs

- Satisfiers

- Dissatisfiers

- Future needs and wants

- Expectations

In obtaining this information, the health department program should decide in advance what level of detail is needed for each of these potential VOC categories. One way to think of the customer's wants and needs is in terms of a Kano model,[3] as shown in Figure 4.5.

The Kano model defined three types of quality:[4]

1. Expected quality, also called basic quality, is the minimum for entry into any market. Because this type of quality goes without saying, it is important to uncover these unstated needs in any customer survey.

2. Normal quality, also called performance quality, is what the customers will state when asked what they want—it is what they specify.

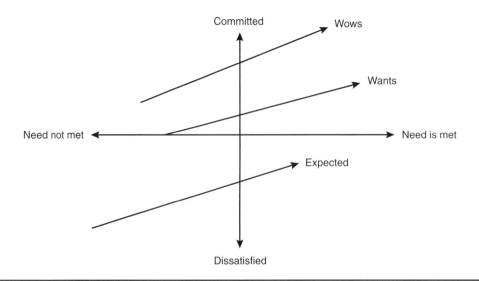

**Figure 4.5**   Kano model.

3. Exciting quality is what delights or wows the customer. It is unexpected by the customer but something they definitely like and will want in the future. This type of quality is something significantly more than the customer expected to experience. One rule to remember is once you wow customers, they will want it the next time.

The Kano model is based on two continuums: (1) the extent to which the customer expectations are met, and (2) the extent to which the customer is committed to the product or service provided. Capturing the voice of the customer, both internal and external, is the first step in using a QFD process and in understanding and interpreting what the customer expects and needs from the function.

Figure 4.6 shows an example of a VOC table. This information can guide you in what to look for when discussing your function's output with a customer. The VOC table identifies six dimensions that are important to understand regarding the function and its alternative uses: who, what, when, where, why, and how of customer use. Alternatives that are uncovered may lead to another set of previously unknown customers. It is important to capture the VOC in their terms and not interpret them until we begin the analysis phase in the table. A customer's verbatim remarks help us understand how the customer interprets the output of our function.

Knowing which requirements are most critical from a customer's perspective is essential when making tradeoffs or sacrificing one requirement to meet another. This process is known as identifying the "critical to quality" (CTQ) requirements. These critical to quality items often cluster around the following seven categories:

- Performance characteristics

- Defect free

- Design/specification limits

| Voice of the customer | Understanding the use of the output of your function | | | | | |
|---|---|---|---|---|---|---|
| | Who | What | When | Where | Why | How |
| Capture the words the customer uses | Who uses it? | What do they use it for? | When do they use it? | Where do they use it? | Why do they use it? | How do they use it? |
| | Who else uses it? | What else could it be used for? | When else could they use it? | Where else could they use it? | Other reasons to use it? | How else could they use it? |

**Figure 4.6**    Understanding/interpreting the voice of the customer.

- Ease of use

- Complexity

- Target values

- Measures and operational definitions

As mentioned earlier in this section, what excites and delights a customer can become a moving target. Critical to quality characteristics are not static. Just as most health departments plan for a community assessment update every three to five years, so should the department update the voice of the customer and the critical to quality analysis on either a scheduled or continuous basis.

The authors have had the privilege of working with a number of local health departments engaged in community assessment activities. Some of the departments plan for and implement a community-wide assessment as a stand-alone event every three to five years. Other departments maintain an ongoing plan of customer segmentation, communication, and voice of the customer inputs as part of their normal operational plan. In the former case, client and community data are updated on a one-time basis across the total community. In the later case, segments of customer data are continually refreshed and decisions are made in a shorter time frame about updating programs and desired outcomes.

The matrix shown in Figure 4.7 is a way to analyze the internal and external customer demands for a function that was uncovered while capturing the VOC.

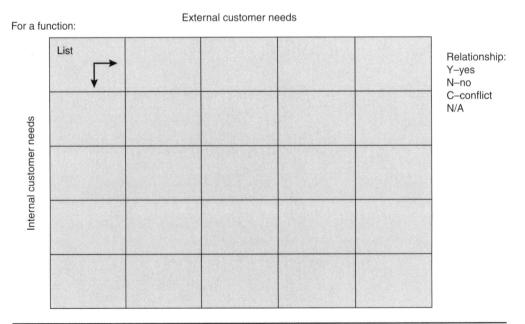

**Figure 4.7**   Understand the overlapping, conflicting, and distinct needs of each customer group.

The purpose of the matrix is to understand the overlapping, conflicting, and distinct needs of each customer group, which may give some insight into determining the critical to quality requirements. The CTQ items are an essential ingredient to be identified as we move into the analysis phase with the QFD matrices.

# SUMMARY

Failure of a function to meet or to consider a major CTQ in the design of a service, program, or process can have a negative impact. Potential external impact can include a decrease in service performance and a significant loss of value to the person served. Potential internal impacts include increased rework or costs and resources wasted on activities that do not address the key priorities of the department.

One of the most powerful tools used in defining CTQs is quality function deployment (QFD). This structured methodology and mathematical tool is used by Lean-Six Sigma practitioners to organize information and prioritize actions. QFD helps transform the VOC into design characteristics, prioritizing each characteristic while simultaneously setting development targets. It helps translate customer requirements into measurable goals. The following chapters amplify the concepts and techniques of both quality function deployment and Lean-Six Sigma and how they support the needs of the public health community.

# ENDNOTES

1. G. Beecroft, G. Duffy, and J. Moran, Editors, *The Executive Guide to Improvement and Change* (Milwaukee, WI: ASQ Quality Press, 2003), p. 148.
2. D. Osborne, "Reinventing Government," *Public Productivity & Management Review,* 16, no. 4 (1993): 349–356.
3. J. ReVelle, J. Moran, and C. Cox, *The QFD Handbook* (New York: John Wiley & Sons, 1998), p. 360.
4. ReVelle, Moran, and Cox, *The QFD Handbook,* pp. 359–365.

# 5

# Process Analysis
# and Waste Reduction

## INTRODUCTION

The essence of Lean-Six Sigma (LSS) is to build a better, faster, more efficient, more effective process. The key components of LSS are:

- **Simplify:** Use 5S to *simplify* the work area (more on this set of tools in Chapter 9).

- **Streamline:** Use spaghetti diagrams and value stream maps to *streamline* the work flow.

- **Optimize:** Use Six Sigma to *focus, improve, sustain, and honor* your progress toward eliminating all defects and deviation.

The authors have observed that the most effective health department improvement teams become obsessed with tweaking existing processes to delight clients, partners, and employees.

Fortunately both the integrated system approach introduced in Chapter 3, the integrated approach model, and LSS have a similar goal—allowing departments to optimize processes to produce better services. The approach of LSS, however, is different from an integrated approach model. LSS has a focus on understanding the flow in processes and how that affects the ability to achieve key objectives. One of the challenges of deploying LSS across a complex organization is that it is labor intensive to gather the data and implement the controls that are recommended by analysis.[1] A major tool for understanding processes for the purpose of optimizing performance is process mapping.

Process mapping is among the most powerful methods that can be used by a QI team to improve a process. Process mapping is important for four

---

We wish to acknowledge Mac McCullough, BS, research assistant and MPH student, University of Minnesota School of Public Health, as co-author of this chapter.

reasons: (1) to understand how a process is structured, (2) to analyze how a process performs, (3) to identify where inefficiencies occur in the process, and (4) to develop ways to improve the process. In this chapter, we will examine each of these four uses. We will also display three types of maps: (1) basic process map, (2) opportunity map, and (3) value stream map (VSM).

## 1. UNDERSTANDING HOW A PROCESS IS STRUCTURED

A *process* is a series of steps taken by an organization to produce an outcome. This is an important way for Public Health to view its work efforts, because all outcomes and outputs in a health department are the result of a specific process. All quality improvement initiatives analyze a process in order to improve performance. A work process has three components:

- It has a beginning point and an end point.

- It uses inputs (people, equipment, supplies, and facilities) to carry out the process.

- It produces an output, which is usually a Public Health service.

For example, a client visit to a childhood immunization clinic involves a multiple-step process. The *beginning point* is when the parent calls for an appointment and the *end point* is when the child and parent leave the clinic after the physician visit. The *inputs* are physicians, nurses, receptionists, exam rooms, equipment, and supplies, while the *output* is a child who has been immunized. The steps in a work process are combined to add value to the inputs by producing a service. In other words, a work process is a series of steps, done in sequence, to produce an outcome.

A typical health department has hundreds, even thousands, of work processes to serve the community. A process improvement team may find it difficult to decide which process to study and how to draw the boundaries for the process. Creating a process map is a disciplined method for overcoming these difficulties as well as understanding and analyzing a process.

## 2. HOW TO ANALYZE A PROCESS

A *process map* is a diagram that displays the main steps in a process and how these steps relate to one another. A process map is the most basic method of analyzing how a process is structured. Different steps are represented by different symbols. The symbols display activity in a process, show the connections, and represent the sequence.

## Creating a Process Map

Creating a process map involves a team of persons from different departments and different disciplines in an organization. This group is known as a quality improvement (QI) team, and it is needed because of the complex nature of most processes. A process may appear simple, but it usually has complexities that not every member of the QI team knows about. By selecting an interdepartmental team, it is possible for each person to see their portion of a process and, more importantly, to see other peoples' parts of a complex process. There are six steps in creating a process map:

### Step 1: Determine the Beginning and End of the Process

The first step for a QI team is to agree where the process starts and where it ends. This step involves determining how extensively the team decides to study a process and how far to follow a process when it crosses into other departments. Ask yourself: What process are we studying? Where does the process start? And where does the process end, or what is the final output?

Another issue is to decide on the process boundaries. *Process boundaries* refer to how far a process will be studied by a QI team. Most processes are linked with related processes. For example, waiting time can be caused by delays in lab tests to determine whether there is a food-borne outbreak. The processes in the laboratory are closely linked to the time required to make a public announcement regarding an outbreak. Delays in a related process will cause delays in the public announcement. A QI team needs to carefully consider where to draw boundaries and how to restrict the extent to which related processes will be studied. Otherwise, the QI team will risk having a scope that is too broad and unachievable.

### Step 2: Determine the Process Steps

The QI team usually begins with a brainstorming session to identify numerous steps. Most processes are cross-functional (go across several departments), and it is important to have members on a QI team from all departments involved in the various process segments. A typical process can have hundreds of steps. A common technique for identifying process steps is to write down each step on a sticky note (one step per note). It is not necessary to go into great detail to identify every step in the process. In fact, it is not useful to try to identify every process step. Rather, just identify key steps and then narrow this down to the 5–10 key steps. Add more steps later, if needed.

Also, ask everyone on the QI team to participate in identifying key steps in the process. One useful aspect of creating a process map is that there is usually no one person who knows all the steps in a process. Some people may think they know all the steps, but are usually surprised to learn that the process does not flow exactly as they believe. Usually, steps have been added and/or deleted without their knowledge.

### Step 3: Sequence the Steps

Once the QI team has agreed on the key steps in a process, the next task is to place the steps in order from the first activity to the last activity. This is why it is helpful to use sticky notes, which can be arranged and rearranged as the team gets more clarity and consensus on how the process works. Move the notes around, placing the first steps at the top of a flipchart sheet and the last step at the bottom. Sequence the steps from start to finish. Be sure to sequence what *is,* not what *should be.*

### Step 4: Draw the Process Map Using the Appropriate Symbols

If you are just learning to flowchart a process, start with the basic symbols shown in Figure 5.1: box, diamond, arrows, and oval.

- Oval—Designates the start and finish of the process.

- Rectangle—Represents a task or activity. It has only one arrow from it.

- Diamond—Designates a decision. Diamonds have two or more arrows leading away. Note that decisions must have a closed loop. This means that no arrow can end with an activity that does not connect again to this process or to a related process. As you gain confidence with flowcharting, add more detailed symbols.

- Arrow—Connects all components of a process

Be consistent in the level of detail shown. A process map can be created with three levels of detail: (1) the macro level, which shows key action steps, but no decision points; (2) the intermediate level, which shows both action and decision points; and (3) the micro level, which shows all details of a process. Make sure all words and acronyms used in the process map are understandable to everyone.

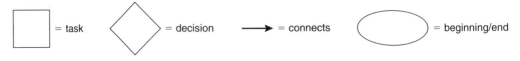

**Figure 5.1**   Basic symbols for a process map.

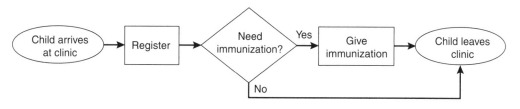

**Figure 5.2**    Basic process map for childhood immunization clinic.

Figure 5.2 shows an example of how these symbols are used to create a process map for a childhood immunization clinic. The ovals show the beginning and ending of the process, the boxes show two activity steps (registration and vaccine administration), and the diamond shows a decision.

The basic process map in Figure 5.2 shows the client entering the clinic (beginning of process), registration (step 1), decision on whether immunization is needed (step 2), administration of the vaccination (step 3), and departure from the clinic (end of process).

## Step 5: Test the Process Map for Completeness

Review all the steps for completeness (correct symbols, closed loops, arrows pointing in the right direction). Make sure the process map is to the right level of detail to explain the process, and identify opportunities or areas for improvement. At this stage the team should ask the following questions: (1) Are symbols used correctly? (2) Are process steps identified clearly? (3) Are all loops closed? (4) Are all continuation points linked elsewhere? (5) Is there one arrow only out of an activity box? (6) Can others follow the process map? Once the team has tested the flowchart by checking these six questions, the chart is ready to finalize and present to others in the organization.

## Step 6: Finalize the Process Map

In this last stage of creating a process map, the QI team looks for problem areas. It is now possible to interpret the process map to study where problems occur in the process and how it can be improved. There are numerous questions to explore once the process map is completed. For example, is the process operating the way it should? Are people following it as designed? Is there complexity or redundancy? How different is the current from the ideal? Where can it be improved? Are there any surprises? Are there concerns?

Once the process map is completed, the team can talk things out. The team will want to confirm conclusions with data. It is also very helpful to communicate with others outside the QI team, showing the chart in order to receive feedback, verification, correction, and comments. A word of advice: Include pertinent information about the chart, including its title, who created it, and when it was created. It will be very useful for future reference. Finally, the QI team may decide to narrow the focus if it is felt that the process boundaries are too broad.

## 3. IDENTIFYING INEFFICIENCIES IN A PROCESS MAP

After a process map has been constructed, it can be analyzed for specific problems. Many times a process map will uncover a problem that cuts across departments. The process map can also identify where a breakdown may occur or where steps can be eliminated. Five types of problems can be identified by studying a process map:

**Disconnect:** A disconnect occurs when a handoff from one group to another is managed poorly. For example, the appointment scheduler makes a client appointment on a day the WIC nutritionist is not in the clinic.

**Bottleneck:** A bottleneck is a point in a process where volume overwhelms capacity. For example, two patients are scheduled during the same appointment time.

**Redundancy:** A redundancy is an activity repeated at two points in a process. An example is when a patient is asked for insurance information at several times (when the appointment is scheduled, when the client arrives for the visit, and when the client is referred to another location for additional services).

**Rework:** Rework is when work is fixed or corrected. For example, if the client insurance information is entered incorrectly or incompletely, extra work is required to retrieve the information later.

**Inspection:** Inspection is a point in the process where appraisal occurs. This usually is a costly extra step and creates potential delay.

## PROCESS FEATURES

Four distinctions are important to keep in mind when preparing and analyzing process maps:

1. **Core Process and support process:** A *core process* is a chain of steps that delivers a service to a patient or community, while a *support process* provides a service to other units within the health

department. Examples of a core process are the infectious disease outbreak unit or WIC program, both of which directly serve the community or clinic. Examples of a support process are the business department, human resources department, and the payroll system, which serve the organization but do not directly serve the client. When quality improvement began in health care, most improvement projects were for support processes. Today, however, the majority of improvement projects are involved with core processes.

2. **The cross functional nature of core process:** Core processes are almost always *cross functional,* which means that many departments are involved in producing a community service. *Cross-functional* means a process goes across two or more departmental units in an organization. For example, in an HIV/AIDS clinic, several departments can be involved, including the appointment-scheduling department, the physician clinic, the lab, and the radiology department.

3. **Process lead time:** The *process lead time* is the total amount of time required to complete a process. For example, the lead time for a childhood immunization is 49 minutes measured from when the child arrives at the clinic until the child departs. Lead time is an important measure of productivity; it is often used as a first clue in a process map to understand problems with a process. Wide variation in lead time indicates that further investigation is needed.

4. **Process and system:** A *process* has been described as a series of steps that transform inputs into a final output. A health care core work process exists in a complex system of numerous processes. The entire health department can be viewed as a series of related processes that, when taken together, form the entire system. A *system* is a series of related processes. Viewed another way, every task that personnel perform in a health department is part of one or more processes.

## TWO TYPES OF PROCESS MAPS

So far this chapter has introduced the process map, shown how to create a process map, and examined several ways that mapping helps problem areas in a process. Now that the basics have been covered, two additional types of process maps will be introduced. Process maps come in different forms depending on the type of problem that needs to be identified. Two other process maps that can be useful for Public Health are (1) the opportunity map and (2) the value stream map.

## Opportunity Map

An opportunity map separates a process map into two components, the "value-added" steps and the "cost-added-only" or "non-value-added" steps. The opportunity flowchart is created by arranging the steps in a process in two sections as shown in Figure 5.3. This opportunity map builds on the process map shown in Figure 5.2 for the childhood immunization clinic and has been expanded to illustrate more tasks in the vaccination of a child. It also has extended the process to include payment for the service by the insurance company. The steps in the left side of the flowchart are needed if the process works perfectly. Steps that exist because of problems and inefficiencies are on the right side of the chart. The right side consists of potentially unnecessary cost-added steps.

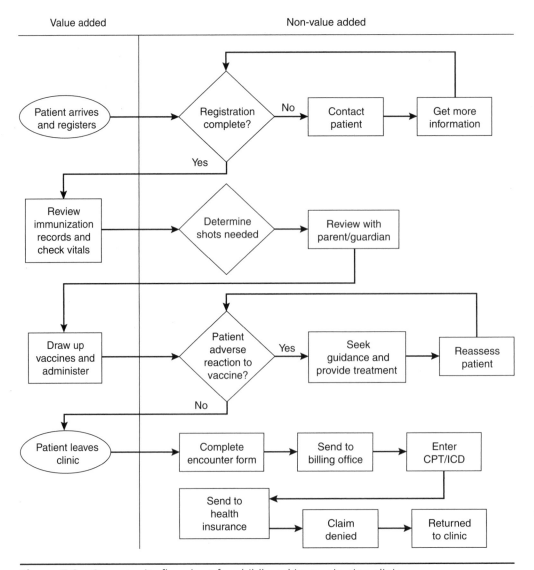

**Figure 5.3**   Opportunity flowchart for childhood immunization clinic.

Once the value-added and non-value-added steps are separated into the two components of the opportunity map, it is possible to inspect the process to eliminate steps that are redundant, backups, or workarounds. While an opportunity map is very helpful in locating inefficiencies, a caveat is warranted. Be careful before labeling a step a cost-added-only step. There may be important reasons why a step was incorporated into a process, and a QI team should be certain before categorizing a step as unnecessary.

## Value Stream Mapping Definitions

A value stream map (VSM) is a special type of process map that examines flow throughout a health department. In order to maximize flow, it is necessary to rely less on the traditional task orientation and look instead at moving a client smoothly through a system. An important aspect of flow is to remove delays in a process. A VSM is an ideal way to illustrate the steps necessary to increase flow.

## Visualizing Patient Flow

A VSM helps visualize patient flow by distinguishing between value-added and non-value-added steps (similar to an opportunity process map) and measuring the amount of time associated with the process steps. A value stream map uses different symbols, and Figure 5.4 shows seven symbols commonly used for illustrating value streams:

1. **Process box:** The process box shows the steps in the process, with additional information regarding time and number of persons involved in the specific steps.

2. **Supporting departments:** Departments that support a process are depicted by a house-shaped box. These departments can include the laboratory, radiology, medical records, and so forth.

3. **Cylinder:** The cylinder represents a database. A VSM usually shows the flow of a client (or tasks) as well as flow of information.

4. **Arrow:** An arrow shows the direction of flow in a process.

5. **Information:** Information is an important component of a value stream map and in relation to process flow.

6. **Triangle:** The triangle depicts the number of clients (or potential number of clients) waiting at each step in the process.

7. **Explosion:** The explosion symbol represents an area in the process targeted for improvement.

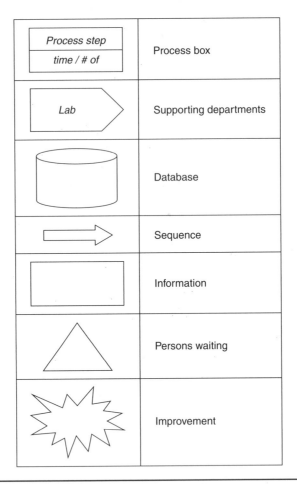

**Figure 5.4**   Flowchart symbols for value stream mapping.

A VSM is typically created with a pencil and eraser, a piece of paper, and a watch to measure *cycle times* (the amount of time to complete each step). A VSM should be created based on direct observation, not from interviews, memory, or an explanation of how a process works. It is inevitable that the manner in which team members think a process works is not how the process works in reality. No matter how familiar team members are with the process, go to the work area and map the value stream by walking from one process step to the next, gathering the required information. We recommend not dividing the process steps among the team members and then trying to piece it together later because none of the team members will get a clear picture of the overall value stream. One or more members of the team should observe the entire process, and the overall team should draw the map based on these observations.

Value stream mapping involves the drawing of two maps, a current-state map and a future-state map. The current-state map illustrates the process as it now works, and the future-state map describes how the process will look once it is improved.

## Current State Value Map

A current state map focuses on one service from beginning to end. If the intent is to map the flow for a childhood immunization clinic, it is not necessary to map the entire WIC program. Mapping other health department processes would make the current state map too complicated to analyze the process of interest.

Figure 5.3 showed an opportunity flowchart for a child immunization clinic. The 18 steps in the process include the arrival of a client at the clinic, the vaccination, the departure, and the follow-up business office activity associated with the visit. The steps are categorized according to value-added steps and non-value-added steps. Next we will convert the information from the opportunity process map into a value stream map. To start the value stream map, we draw four process steps and their related information. An inefficiency is indicated when clients wait between each process step. Clients waiting at each process step are represented by a triangle, with numbers that indicate the minimum and maximum number of patients being pushed from one step to the next.

In a VSM the number of steps is reduced to the major steps in the process. The four value-added steps are: client registration, a clinical review of the immunization records, vaccine administration, and patient departure.

Because the flow of information is just as important as the flow of patients, information flow is also added to a value stream map. Having clients and providers at a specific process step without the information to provide service is another form of waste and is non-value added. Information flow begins when an appointment is scheduled for a child's immunization. Patient demographic information is uploaded to a database during the scheduling process. When electronic transmission is relayed by means other than data entry to database, the methods should be identified adjacent to the information arrow (such as phone, Internet, or fax). The final step in the process involves administering the immunizations. All pertinent immunization review and consent forms have been secured, and the mapping of the entire value stream is now complete. The map includes both the physical flow of the child receiving the immunization as well as the information flow and depicts the entire process from the scheduling of the initial visit until payment is received for the service.

Additional valuable information can be added to this value stream map to identify the process performance. A time line is drawn at the bottom of the map to indicate the beginning and end of each process. A value stream map and time line are shown in Figure 5.5. The actual time for each step (cycle time) is indicated on the time line below the process box. *Wait times* are noted on the time line between process boxes. The sum of all process times (cycle time + wait time) equals the time required to provide the service. The *lead time* is defined as the total time to deliver the service and is calculated by adding all the values on the time line. In other words, lead time is the time it takes to process a patient through the entire value stream.

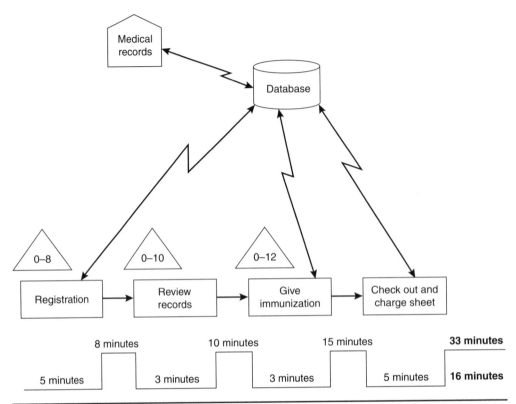

**Figure 5.5**   Current state value stream map for childhood immunization clinic.

Lead time and value-added time are used to calculate the efficiency of the process. The *process efficiency percentage* (PEP) is defined as the percentage of the total process time that is value added. It is calculated by dividing the value-added time by the lead time and converting to a percentage. In this example, the value-added time is 16 minutes, non-value-added time is 33 minutes, and the lead time is 49 minutes (value-added + non-value-added = 16 + 33). The process efficiency percentage is calculated as follows:

$$PEP = \frac{\text{Value Added Time}}{\text{Lead Time}} = \frac{16 \text{ minutes}}{49 \text{ minutes}} = 33\%$$

## Future State Value Map

The future state value map depicts the ideal value stream and is a planned representation of an ideal future state. A future state map maximizes the value-added steps and minimizes the lead time. The future state map should eliminate as many non-value-added steps as possible. An example of a future state map for the childhood immunization clinic is shown in Figure 5.6. Several features in the future state map illustrate improved performance of the process. First, the map no longer includes triangles between the process boxes. Next, notice that the information flow has

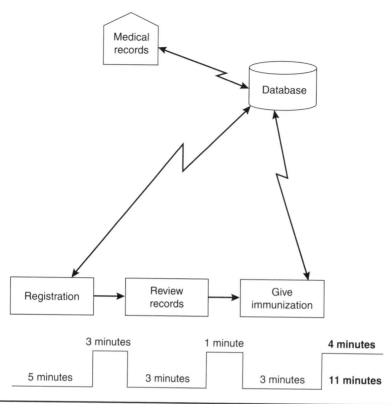

**Figure 5.6**   Future state value stream map for childhood immunization clinic.

not changed; if there have been no problems with the information flow then the value stream map can stay the same. The lead time to complete the entire process is now 15 minutes (a 69% reduction from the current process of 49 minutes) while the value-added time is now 4 minutes (a 75% reduction from the current process of 16 minutes). This improvement was achieved by eliminating the final step in the process (checkout and charge submission), less time to perform value-added steps, and reducing the wait times between value-added steps. While the process efficiency percentage (PEP) is now 27%, the overall process requires much less time for the client. The reduced PEP suggests there is more improvement opportunity. This is an example of continual improvement: Once the gain in quality and efficiency is made, go to the next level and improve it again.

## SPAGHETTI DIAGRAM

A spaghetti diagram is a drawing of client and staff flow that illustrates how the immunization clinic operates in a Public Health clinic.[2] The example in Figure 5.7 shows the flow in a childhood immunization clinic: The client enters the clinic, then goes to the receptionist, to the waiting room to complete registration forms, to the receptionist to drop off completed forms, and so forth.

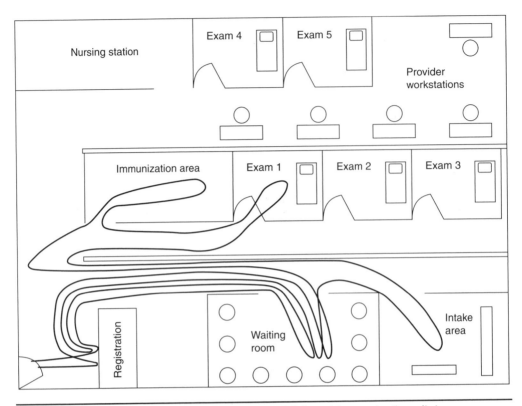

**Figure 5.7** Spaghetti diagram for a patient at childhood immunization clinic.

The diagram in Figure 5.8 shows the movement of the provider who examines the child and administers the vaccine. It also shows the movement of the medical records. In this case, a separate staff member physically carried the records from the medical records office into the immunization area.

Tracing the movement of the client and provider can be valuable in identifying inefficiency, delay, and barriers to flow. For example, we can see in Figure 5.8 that the provider visited with the patient in exam room 1, but then went into exam room 2 to visit another patient. Perhaps this could be due to the waiting time necessary for the medical records to be brought to the immunization area. Spaghetti diagrams can help uncover inefficiencies by shedding light on client or provider movement or other aspects of the process that might not be entirely apparent from the process map.

## VALUE-ADDED VERSUS TIME CHART

A VSM can be used to show how value is added and the time required as the client (or task) flows through a process (see Figure 5.9). In plotting value-added time, anything that adds value to the process/task moves the line up the chart.[3]

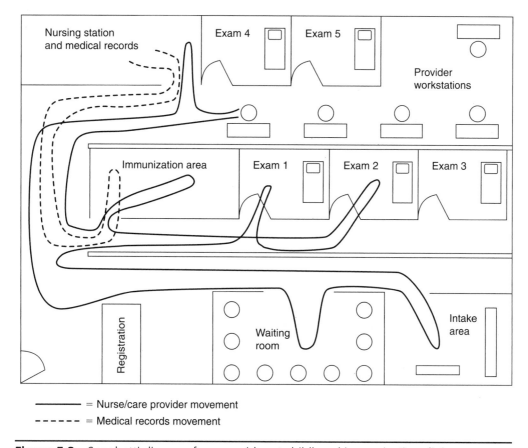

**Figure 5.8** Spaghetti diagram for a provider at childhood immunization clinic.

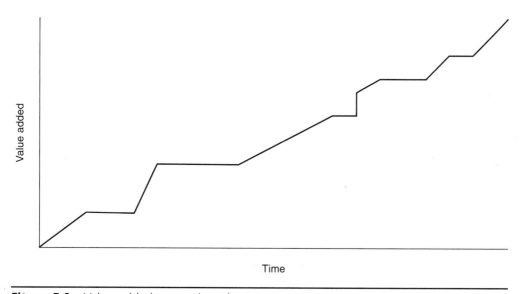

**Figure 5.9** Value-added versus time chart.

When no value is added, the line is horizontal. For example, when the client is waiting, no value is added. The scaling on a value-added versus time chart is notional. Flat periods help identify delay, while vertical lines help identify the amount and speed of the value-added services.

# THE EIGHT TYPES OF WASTE

The eight types of waste are a quick method of engaging teams in an improvement project. A simple technique is to create a laminated card containing a list with definitions of the eight types of waste. This reference card becomes a visual aid as team members brainstorm and as a communication engagement tool from which team members can share with their coworkers while engaging in their daily work.

The idea is to eliminate as many of these types of waste as possible. Removal makes additional time and resources available for higher priority outcomes of the department. The eight types of waste are explained in Table 5.1.

# SUMMARY

Understanding process performance is an important first step in ensuring that Public Health services are delivered efficiently and effectively. This chapter introduced several techniques for analyzing processes:

1. Process map

2. Opportunity process map

3. Value stream map

4. Spaghetti diagram

5. Value-added versus time chart

When these techniques are applied systematically, it is possible to identify five types of inefficiencies from a process map and eight types of waste from a value stream map. The process efficiency percentage (PEP) can be calculated by analyzing cycle time, lead time, and value-added time.

A process map has many important uses. First, it identifies major action steps and decisions in a process. If the QI team does not have an accurate understanding of the important steps in a process, it will not be able to study or improve the process. A process map allows the team to identify the sequence of events in a process and to understand it. Second, process mapping shows the difference

**Table 5.1**    Eight types of waste.

| Waste | Description | Public health example |
|---|---|---|
| Overproduction | Items being produced in excess quantity and products being made before the customer needs them | Insurance filing or immunization record opened before all required information is received |
| Waiting | Periods of inactivity in a downstream process that occur because an upstream activity does not produce or deliver on time | Paperwork waiting for management signature or review |
| Unnecessary motion | Extra steps taken by employees and equipment to accommodate inefficient process layouts | Immunology testing equipment stored in cabinets far from specialist's work area |
| Transportation handling | Unnecessary movement of materials or double handling | Department vehicles stored in central facility, requiring constant movement of vehicles to and from other high-traffic locations |
| Overprocessing | Spending more time than necessary to produce the product or service | Combining client survey instruments into one form rather than develop specific instruments for each program |
| Unnecessary inventory | Any excess inventory that is not directly required for the current client's order | Overestimating vaccination support materials, requiring additional locked storage cages, inventory counting, and reconciliation |
| Defects | Errors produced during a service transaction or while developing a product | Ineffective scripts for initial intake applications. Unclear directions for filling out forms |
| Duplication | Having to reenter data or repeat details on forms | Poorly designed client intake computer screens or services checklists |

between what people think happens and what actually happens. It is very rare for a person or group in Public Health to accurately understand how a process works until a process map has been created. The process map shows unexpected complexity, problem areas, and redundancy that would be difficult to otherwise detect. Third, process mapping allows the team to agree on the steps and study activities that may affect performance improvement. Fourth, it allows the QI team to compare the actual process versus the ideal process. Finally, it identifies where breakdowns may occur or where steps can be eliminated, and it identifies areas where data can be collected.

# ENDNOTES

1. L. Gibbs and T. Shea, "The Power of Two: Combining Lean Six Sigma and BPM," *BPTrends Magazine* (April 2007).
2. T. M. Kubiak and D. W. Benbow, *The Certified Six Sigma Black Belt Handbook,* 2nd ed. (Milwaukee, WI: ASQ Quality Press, 2009).
3. A. C. Smith, R. Barry, and C. E. Brubaker, "Going Lean: Busting Barriers to Patient Flow." *ACHE Management Series* (Chicago: Health Administration Press, 2007).

# 6

# Using the Language of Senior Management: The Bottom Line

## INTRODUCTION: SHOW ME THE MONEY

The language of senior management is the language of money. Public Health departments run on budgets just as private corporations do. "Not-for-profit" does not mean that everything is free. Government and municipal programs need funding just like any other resource-based activity. Chapter 3, "An Integrated QI Approach," describes the alignment of functional activities within the department to the voice of the customer. Department activities are identified during the annual budget planning cycle. It is this budget cycle that puts a financial valuation to customer requirements. The bottom line drives not-for-profit organizations just as much as private corporations.

Senior management is also responsible for the strategic direction of the Public Health department. Community-wide assessments, such as the National Association of County & City Health Officials *Mobilizing for Action through Planning and Partnerships* process,[1] are discussed in earlier chapters as channels for the voice of the customer foundation of quality function deployment. This voice of the customer generates critical to quality requirements that drive the inputs to department strategy.

Senior management is responsible to define, communicate, refine, and implement a clear and focused strategy, based on a thorough understanding of target customers' expectations. Management expert Peter Drucker observed that strategy has to move and be refined at a speed comparable to what used to be called *tactics*; it has to be in real time.[2] The process of aligning department requirements to the voice of the customer is a major component of the Macro phase of the continuous quality improvement (CQI) system in Public Health.

Strategic management creates a strategy for the organization using external information about the economic environment and from clients, the community, funding bodies, and other stakeholders. Internal information regarding existing resources and capabilities, as well as the existing strategy, is also taken into account. The strategy guides the design and development of new programs or services or improves existing programs.

All activities within a specific department depend on one another as a result of direct links to the voice of the customer. These links come from the Macro to Meso to Micro planning sequence and are the basis for the process design. Once the process steps and activities are identified within a program, responsibilities are assigned to the individual for daily management. CQI becomes the never-ending process of standardization and improvement, as shown in Figure 1.9, "Continuous Quality Improvement System in Public Health."

The leadership style and organizational structure of the health department guides the translation of these external and internal requirements into functional areas such as environmental health, immunization clinics, emergency preparedness, and substance abuse assigned to managers within the department. This translation takes place during the Meso phase of the CQI system.

Unit managers work with their staff to organize projects and ongoing programs during the Micro phase of the CQI system. These annual planning sessions generate processes that comprise the daily operations of a health

---

**Soaring Eagle Clinic 2010 Operating Budget**

**Expense projections**

**Variable Costs**

| Personnel | | FTE | Hours | VC | TVC |
|---|---|---|---|---|---|
| Clinic | | 23.76 | 47995.2 | $ 32.00 | $1,535,846 |
| Lab | | 1 | 2020 | $ 21.00 | $    42,420 |
| X-ray | | 1 | 2020 | $ 18.00 | $    36,360 |
| | Total | **25.76** | **52035.2** | | **$1,614,626** |

| Supplies | | | Quantity | VC | TVC |
|---|---|---|---|---|---|
| Clinic | | | 42000 | $ 10.00 | $  420,000 |
| Lab | | | 38000 | $ 15.00 | $  570,000 |
| X-ray | | | 15000 | $ 30.00 | $  450,000 |
| | Total | | **95000** | | **$1,440,000** |

**Fixed Costs**

| Overhead, PPE | | | | | $  500,000 |
|---|---|---|---|---|---|

| **Total Costs** | | | | | **$3,554,626** |
|---|---|---|---|---|---|

**Figure 6.1**   Initial projection of annual operating budget expenses.

department. Once unit operations are defined, monitoring systems are established to maintain the quality of the programs and services provided to clients and other stakeholders.

One effective way to engage senior management in quality improvement activities is to put dollar signs on the outcomes. Budgeting is a major tool used by unit managers to develop quality plans. A program budget for a health department consists of fixed costs and variable costs.

Figure 6.1 is an example of a summary operating budget projection for a county health clinic. Senior department management knows how to read this report. The next section of this chapter shows an example of how to identify the costs related to QI activities and how those costs impact the effectiveness of the department. Figure 6.1 contains a program-level budget projection that corresponds with the overall operation of the clinic. A health department senior planning meeting might start at this level of financial estimation to allocate major cost categories aligned with key client segments. At this point administrative and support process activities such as training and QI are not specifically itemized.

## THE EXTERNALLY VERSUS INTERNALLY FOCUSED ORGANIZATION

It can be a challenge to choose priority improvement areas and clearly present them to management. One common approach is to look at cost, quality, and service. Another way is to group cost, quality, and productivity. The former approach takes an external view based on client and community service needs. The latter approach addresses internal operational issues such as resource utilization and personnel capacity.

The two approaches are often visualized as triangles with the components weighted more or less equally, as shown in Figure 6.2. Sometimes all are linked together via costs in an attempt to make a complex situation clear. The externally focused model in Figure 6.2 shows arrows pointing from inside the circle representing the health department outward to interact with the client, community, other components of the Public Health system, and stakeholders. While cost and quality are key components of both models, the externally focused model stresses service and the internally focused model stresses productivity.

The internally focused model shows arrows pointing from outside into the organization, which is composed of the personnel, operations, and technology that support internal department functions. Like the externally focused model, quality, and cost are key components of the internally focused model. However, the objective of the third component, productivity, is to get the most outputs as viewed from the perspective of the organization (rather than the external stakeholder).

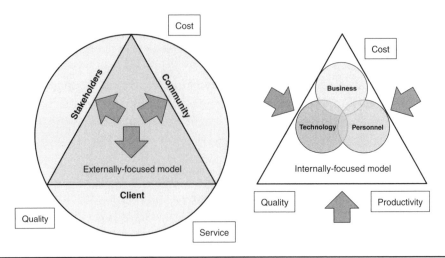

**Figure 6.2**  Externally versus internally focused costing approaches.

As health departments become more customer oriented, they will gravitate to the externally focused model for visualizing costs associated with running the organization. Although the cost activities may be the same, the perspective changes to being driven by external client touch points rather than internal functional processes. This difference in perspective pulls health department leadership into a more strategic, integrated management style that stresses the cross-functional impact of resource utilization. This perspective is contrary to the traditional silo mentality found in many organizations where each function protects its budget. The problem with the silo approach is that when each unit maximizes its own productivity, the overall productivity of an organization can actually decrease and external client requirements remain unmet.

## IDENTIFY THE BOTTOM LINE

An effective way to align client and community requirements to organizational goals is to begin with the department budget. The annual budget is the reality of what the health department has to work with to serve the community. Figure 6.3 is a portion of the Soaring Eagle Clinic's 2010 operating budget, which has been developed from the initial expense projections shown in Figure 6.1.

The pro forma snapshot for Soaring Eagle Clinic illustrates how the strategic planning process translates funding resources and expenses into tactical plans for each program. These plans are reflected by monthly budgets so that managers can monitor and control operations. This high-level summary of funding sources and related expenses also provides the basis for leadership to allocate resources to individual projects and units. Initial planning frequently identifies significant shortfalls in ability to provide desired services. The negative value of the project surplus in Figure 6.3 is an example of when expenses exceed available funding.

**Soaring Eagle Clinic 2010—Pro Forma**

**Operating Budget**

**Revenues**

| | | |
|---|---|---|
| Clinic visits | | $1,806,000 |
| Lab | | $ 456,000 |
| Radiology | | $ 330,000 |
| | Total | $2,592,000 |

**Expenses**

| | | |
|---|---|---|
| Variable costs | | |
| Labor | | $1,614,626 |
| Supplies | | $1,440,000 |
| | Total | $3,054,626 |

| | | |
|---|---|---|
| Contrib. margin | | −$ 462,626 |
| Fixed costs | | $ 500,000 |

| | |
|---|---|
| **Projected surplus** | −$ 962,626 |

**Figure 6.3**    Soaring Eagle Clinic 2010 operating statement.

Once the strategic planning process has identified what the department will focus on for the year, individual function managers use the resources that have been allocated to their units to create programs for the community and clients. Each manager is allocated a certain amount of fixed costs ($500,000 in the example shown in Figure 6.3) for space, equipment, utilities, and so on. The projected variable cost of anticipated programs, projects, and ongoing operations are also divided among the functional managers ($2,574,009 in the Soaring Eagle example of Figure 6.3) to be parsed out as services to client and community requirements.

As described in Chapter 2, "Introduction to Quality Function Deployment and Lean-Six Sigma," and Chapter 3, "An Integrated QI Approach," the cascaded matrices of quality function deployment (QFD) provide an effective stairway management can use to decompose the fixed and variable expenses of the strategic budget into operational cost categories directly related to individual projects and programs.

So how does the functional manager translate the financial language of senior management into manageable activities for staff? QFD starts with a defined process for the activities that must be performed. This is the connection between the Macro, Meso, and Micro levels of the CQI system for Public Health. The alignment model described in Chapter 3 shows goals and objectives flowing from senior management to functional managers, who then work closely with the front-line staff to set tasks, measures, and time lines for delivering services to the community to meet the indicated voice of the customer as identified during initial QFD activities.

Figure 6.4 is a process map created by the Orange County, FL, Health Department (OCHD) for its Child Immunization Program. This effort was part of a set of integrated improvement projects in 2009 using Lean-Six Sigma techniques by the Strategic Planning Department at OCHD. One of the authors was the Master Black Belt facilitator and trainer for this integrated quality system pilot. The process map is in a format called a "deployment flowchart," which shows the people or departments responsible and the flow of the process steps or tasks they are assigned. The four columns in the deployment flowchart show the process steps for the client, clerk, nurse, and billing clerk. This format is useful to clarify roles and track accountability as well as to indicate dependencies in the sequence of events.[3] Figure 6.4 is a fourth type of process map, which supplements the basic flowchart, opportunity flowchart, and value stream map discussed in Chapter 5's "Process Analysis and Waste Reduction" section.

The deployment map gives a level of detail that allows the identification of labor and supplies costs that must come out of the major variable costing lines in an OCHD version of the pro forma profit and loss statement shown in Figure 6.3.

The summary worksheet in Figure 6.5 shows the activities for each of the four persons identified in the deployment map. These activities to perform child immunizations are summed into a total using hourly rates of the individuals involved multiplied by the time required to complete the task. In this example, only person hours were included in the planned and actual columns. Where supplies and equipment are not already included in administrative costs, these would be priced into the summary worksheet as well. The value stream map described in Chapter 5's "Reduction of Defects and Variation" section provides additional detail on cycle time, resource usage, and personnel hours for the major steps in the child immunization process. Additional information on value stream mapping is available in *The Lean Six Sigma Pocket Tool Book*.[4]

For this example, the OCHD quality coordinator and one of the authors used the flowchart summary form in Figure 6.5 to separate activity costs by the categories listed in the lefthand column of the chart. For confidentiality reasons, hypothetical costs have been included in the worksheet. The costs are organized by the function performing the activity and accumulated into columns using the same titles as the deployment process map (flowchart) shown in Figure 6.4.

The actual cost of providing child immunizations at OCHD are totaled by category and compared with the requested budget categories for each department. The delta column is an indicator of an over- or underspending condition. A delta condition suggests an action item to discover what caused the gap between expected and actual resources required for this category of activity, time, or resource.

The bottom rows in Figure 6.5 can now be explained. Measurement units refer to how the category is measured in order to affix a dollar amount to the resource used. Usually this unit is based on the original costing unit of the item, such as reams of copier paper, average hourly wage, and cost per square foot of office space. Partnerships needed may require consideration of indirect costs, such as consultants' fees or special recognition expenses for community-based partners sponsoring a faith-based immunization drive.

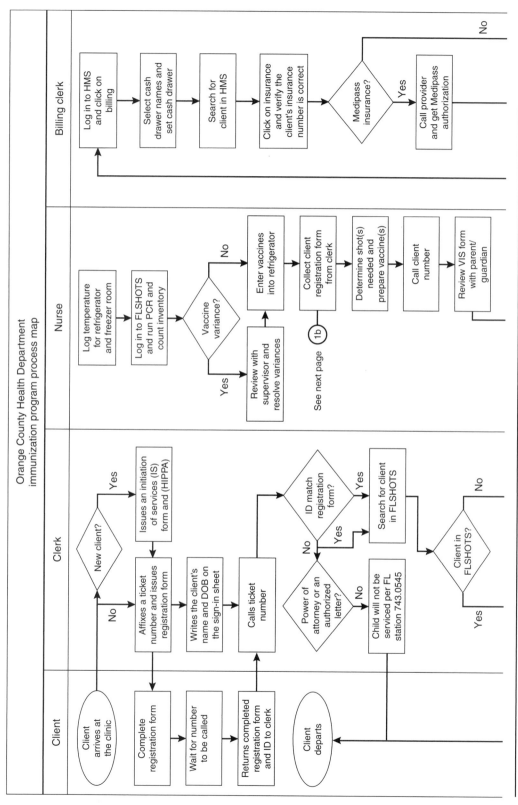

**Figure 6.4** Orange County Health Department immunization map.

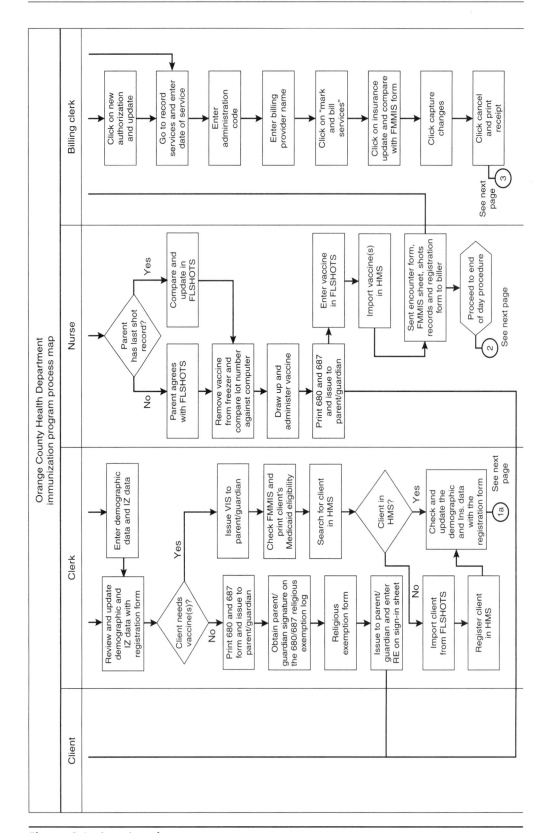

**Figure 6.4** *(continued)*

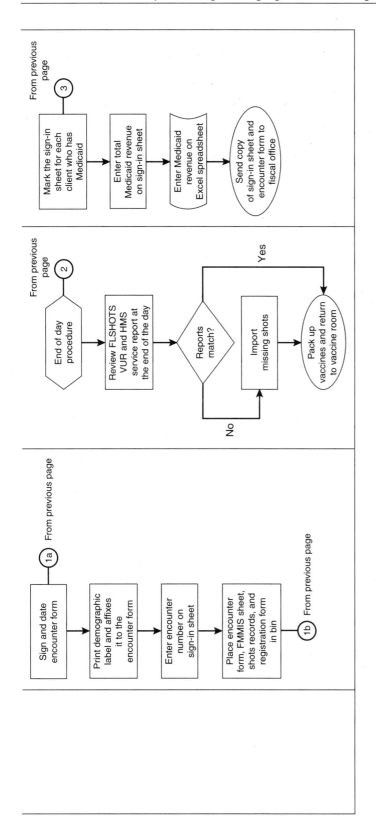

| Flow chart function | Client | Clerk | Nurse | Billing clerk | Supervisor | Σ | Actual | Delta |
|---|---|---|---|---|---|---|---|---|
| Cost | Not included | $3.11 | $1.97 | $2.07 | $0.79 | $7.94 | $11.42 | $3.48 |
| Person hours | | .3 hr × $10.35 | .1 hr × $19.68 | .2 hr × $10.35 | .05 × $15.71 | | | |
| Supplies required | ID, POA, authorization form | Sign-in sheet, registration form, demographics label, RE log, lobby ticket, shot record, VIS, paper, pencils, clip board, encounter form, 680, 687, Init of svc, HIPPA form, HMS, "blue", "white" cards | Vaccines, needles, sanitary materials, vaccine prep and transport materials | Admin code list, interoffice envelope, receipt forms | | | | |
| Equipment required | Sunk cost | I/T services, bin, phone, FLSHOTS, FMMI, printer, terminal, copier, fax machine, communication lines | Refrig, I/S access, HMS, terminal, desk, chairs, VUR, PIR, FLSHOTS | HMS, I/T services, Excel, desk phone, printer | | | | |
| Space required | Sunk cost | Lobby, reception desk, clerk area, rest rooms | Freezer, immunization and vaccine rooms | Fiscal office | | | | |
| Time | Travel, lobby queue, apply, vaccination | | | | Escalation | | | |
| CoQ–P –A –F (I, E) | Rework, duplicate records, errors in app | | | | | | | |
| Partnerships needed | NA | | | | | | | |
| Measurement unit | Cycle time, #/day # in queue | | | | | | | |

Type of step: P–process, D–decision, T–transport, W–wait, S–storage

Flow chart costing summary: Orange County, Florida child immunization
© Moran, Duffy 8/25/09

**Figure 6.5**    OCHD child immunization process costing summary worksheet.

The cost of quality row is a valuable category for senior leadership committed to continuous improvement. As indicated in Chapter 5's "Reduction of Defects and Variation" section, the concept of Lean-Six Sigma is to constantly seek to eliminate all sources of waste within the organization. Except for row 7, all the rows in Figure 6.5 identify the cost of community programs and client services. However, row 7, cost of quality (COQ), highlights costs incurred by the department because the process is not working as designed or because the designed process is flawed and waste is being produced in the normal course of this activity.

## COST OF QUALITY OVERVIEW

Joseph M. Juran defined COQ as "the sum of all costs that would disappear if there were no quality problems."[5] This definition implies that COQ represents the difference between the actual cost of a program or service and what the cost would have been if everyone satisfied requirements 100% of the time.[6] From this viewpoint, quality costs could be regarded as wasted resources that cannot be put to productive use for the community. In 1943, Armand V. Feigenbaum suggested quality costs could be separated into four categories: prevention cost (PC), appraisal cost (AC), internal failure cost (IFC), and external failure cost (EFC).[7] The four kinds of quality costs are not independent of one another, and a trade-off exists among the four categories of quality costs.[8] For example, an increase in PC and AC would result in the decrease of the IFC and EFC.[9,10]

COQ usually follows what is called the PAF model. It is a means of classifying costs of an organization into costs associated with *prevention* of quality defects, costs to perform *appraisal* of quality, and costs from *failures,* both internal (before service delivery) and external failures. These costs' ratios vary from industry to industry. The P:A:F ratio is typically 1:4:12, but this ratio has not yet been calculated for a Public Health department.

For a Public Health department wishing to start a COQ implementation, the PAF costs are tracked either monthly or quarterly. Improvement activities come from applying any improvement methodology. Initial work is usually focused on increasing prevention activities or refocusing activities into areas of high failure cost. When PAF improvement begins, there is often a 10% reduction in total measured PAF costs each year. Over time, appraisal activities may decline due to reduced incidence of failure. After 8 to 10 years, improvements level off. The program then enters a status quo phase, to hold the gains and institutionalize the systems developed through improvement activities.

Most COQ measures are established as a ratio to funding or some other department measure of volume. This allows tracking real gains; that is, gains are adjusted for new funding (or for loss of funding).

It is useful to note that the measured PAF costs are rarely the majority of the costs of quality; many costs are hidden in overhead and are not easily tracked. Every function typically generates some quality costs. These are "indirect costs" incurred by various overhead departments, typically reacting to events of non-conformance, such as rework on an activity or billing errors. Such costs are often accepted as the cost of doing business, but if properly identified and monitored, they can become a target for improvement. It should not be enough to know they are occurring. By working on the root causes of the measured costs, these invisible costs can be reduced. These hidden costs should be monitored by the manager accountable for the activity where the failures occur.

Figure 6.6 is a revised version of the OCHD Immunization Flowchart Summary Form with estimates of cost of quality gains related to the future state value stream mapping described in Chapter 5's "Reduction of Defects and Variation" section. The third row from the bottom shows the COQ is reduced by lowering stress on the staff caused by long client wait times, resulting in fewer mistakes and less rework, saving 45 minutes of internal failure time a day of clerical review and correction. Smoother flow of clients through the clinic provides better organization for the nurses, returning an hour of appraisal time required to monitor equipment and supplies either at the beginning or the end of the shift. The billing clerk saves another 36 minutes of internal failure time each day searching for unfiled paperwork. On the "expense" side of the cost of quality equation is 15 minutes each morning the clerical supervisor invests in reviewing the anticipated demands of the day and checking with the clinical staff to make sure all is ready before clients arrive for immunization procedures. The 15 minutes of prevention time is more than justified by the $33.65 savings in failure and appraisal time removed from the process by eliminating significant wait times. The resulting gain of $29.72 per day of staff time to dedicate to other pressing activities can be annualized to an approximate labor saving value of $7,727.

Although the methods exist to track the hidden costs of quality, it is not frequently done in practice. The major reason for not tracking COQ is lack of management interest and support coupled with the belief that quality costing is "paperwork" that does not contribute value. Other major reasons for not tracking COQ are a lack of knowledge how to track costs and benefits of COQ as well as a lack of adequate accounting and computer systems. Given the advances in data collection, storage, and retrieval systems, these reasons are no longer as valid for not reporting COQ.

## CONTRIBUTIONS OF COST OF QUALITY

A major benefit of having COQ information is that cost and outcomes can become common ground, especially for turning quality jargon into the language of management. COQ emphasizes prevention over appraisal and both prevention

| Flow chart function | Client | Clerk | Nurse | Billing clerk | Supervisor | Σ | Actual | Delta |
|---|---|---|---|---|---|---|---|---|
| Cost | Not included | $3.11 | $1.97 | $2.07 | $0.79 | $7.94 | $11.42 | $3.48 |
| Person hours | | .3 hr × $10.35 | .1 hr × $19.68 | .2 hr × $10.35 | .05 × $15.71 | | | |
| Supplies required | ID, POA, authorization form | Sign-in sheet, registration form, demographics label, RE log, lobby ticket, shot record, VIS, paper, pencils, clip board, encounter form, 680, 687, Init of svc, HIPPA form, HMS, "blue", "white" cards | Vaccines, needles, sanitary materials, vaccine prep and transport materials | Admin code list, interoffice envelope, receipt forms | | | | |
| Equipment required | Sunk cost | I/T services, bin, phone, FLSHOTS, FMMI, printer, terminal, copier, fax machine, communication lines | Refrig, I/S access, HMS, terminal, desk, chairs, VUR, PIR, FLSHOTS | HMS, I/T services, Excel, desk phone, printer | | | | |
| Space required | Sunk cost | Lobby, reception desk, clerk area, rest rooms | Freezer, immunization and vaccine rooms | Fiscal office | | | | |
| Time | Travel, lobby queue, apply, vaccination | | | | Escalation | | | |
| CoQ–P –A –F (I, E) | Rework, duplicate records, errors in app | IF = .75 × $10.35 = $7.76 | A = 1.0 × $19.68 = $19.68 | IF = .60 × $10.35 = $6.21 | P = .25 × 15.71 = $3.93 | 7.76 19.68 6.21 33.65 –3.93 $29.72 | | |
| Partnerships | NA | | | | | | | |
| Measurement unit | Cycle time, #/day # in queue | | | | | | | |

Type of step: P–process, D–decision, T–transport, W–wait, S–storage

Flow chart costing summary: Orange County, Florida child immunization
© Moran, Duffy 8/25/09

**Figure 6.6** OCHD immunization flowchart process costing with COQ estimates.

and appraisal for better management of failure costs. Using a summary chart such as that developed for the child immunization process provides a quick way to show financial impact to senior management. Not only are the costs of running a program as designed shown on the chart, but the costs of waste and errors are provided through the four COQ categories. The intent for showing such a summary to senior management is (1) to track actual expenses for budgeted program operations and (2) to identify costs that can be eliminated through process improvement activities.

The goal of COQ is to eliminate all external failure costs, minimize or eliminate internal failure cost, and balance the use of resources for appraisal of activities to ensure that they are performing as expected. The most effective use of an investment in quality is in prevention. Similar to encouraging clients to live healthy lifestyles, designing effective programs, training employees to do it right the first time, and preventing unnecessary cost is the least expensive approach for running a Public Health department.

## SELLING COQ TO LEADERSHIP

The value of including the COQ concept in planning and implementing effective health departments can be summarized as:

1. An ounce of prevention is worth a pound of cure.

2. You can control only what you measure.

3. Right measures drive right behavior.

4. COQ provides a direct link from quality activities to the accounting statements.[11]

Chapter 7, "Milestones and Measures, Interim and Final Reporting," offers additional approaches for effectively meeting the needs of the health department through gathering, analyzing, reporting, and tracking activities based on objectives and data.

## THE BOTTOM LINE FEEDS BACK TO THE TOP LINE: USE QFD TO VALIDATE VOC

By now the reader should be seeing circles and feedback loops in each chapter of this text. Like the PDCA/SDCA cycle described in Chapter 1, unless a feedback loop is directly tied to the initial objective of the activity, there is no clear way for senior leadership to measure the outcome of a process. The old saying "What goes around, comes around" is true. The voice of the customer is the input to the first stage of QFD. Senior management is responsible to both the client and the health department for meeting the stated needs of the client and community.

The tools of lean and Six Sigma offer a dependable structure for each functional unit to operate effectively as the VOC is translated into the technical language of the department.

Money is the common language of business, whether it is a private corporation, a not-for-profit organization, or a government agency. Putting dollar signs on activities balances the differences in value perception between client and service provider. Identifying errors and waste in dollars lost or saved gets immediate attention in a report. The budget represents the financial resources available to meet client needs (which are the top line for the organization). QFD and the tools of Lean-Six Sigma combine to tie the top and bottom lines together for maximum effectiveness.

# ENDNOTES

1. Mobilizing for Action through Planning and Partnerships (MAPP), http://www.naccho.org/topics/infrastructure/MAPP/index.cfm (accessed July 12, 2009). MAPP is a community-driven strategic planning tool for improving community health.
2. E. H. Edersheim, *The Definitive Drucker* (McGraw-Hill, 2007), p. 39.
3. *The Public Health Memory Jogger II* (Salem, NH: GOAL/QPC and the Public Health Foundation, 2007), p. 61.
4. M. L. George, D. P. Rowlands, M. Price, and J. Maxey, *The Lean Six Sigma Pocket Tool Book* (New York: McGraw-Hill, 2005), 45–49.
5. J. M. Juran, *Quality Control Handbook*, 3rd ed. (New York: McGraw-Hill, 1974).
6. H. J. Harrington, "Performance Improvement: A Total Poor-Quality Cost System," *The TQM Magazine,* Vol. 11, no. 4 (1999), 221–230.
7. A. V. Feigenbaum, *Total Quality Control*, 3rd ed. (New York: McGraw-Hill, 1983).
8. F. M. Gryna, "Quality and Cost," *Juran's Quality Handbook*, Joseph M. Juran and A. Blanton Godfrey, eds., 5th ed. (New York: McGraw-Hill, 1999).
9. H. J. Harrington, *Poor-Quality Cost* (Milwaukee, WI: Marcel Dekker/ASQC Quality Press, 1987).
10. Q. S. Jing-hua Shi and L. Sheng-jie, "The Power of Balance, Studying Trade Off Relationships to Calculate Cost of Quality" (by Quality Progress Magazine, February 2009).
11. D. C. Wood, *The Executive Guide to Understanding and Implementing Quality Cost Programs* (Milwaukee, WI: ASQ Quality Press, 2007).

# 7

# Milestones and Measures: Interim and Final Reporting

## INTRODUCTION

Quality function deployment (QFD) provides an ideal foundation for the department measurement system. QFD ties internal activities within the department to expectations of the client and other stakeholders, providing a line of sight from individual activity back to the strategic plan. Figure 3.4 tracks the flow of policy deployment throughout the organization, culminating in measures and indicators supporting individual tasks. The data resulting from these measures and monitoring activities is fed back through the organization on a continuous basis for interim tracking and adjustment. Final outcomes are also measured for reporting and long term assessment.

Figure 7.1 is a partial re-creation of Figure 3.1, the QFD/VOC integrated fulfillment approach. The critical client priorities identified in the "Client Requirements to Design Requirements" block of Figure 7.1 are the major outcomes of the organization. These outcomes need to be measured in a way that allows senior leadership to know whether the health department is on course with the strategy developed to meet those outcomes.

The adage "If you can't measure it, you can't manage it" comes to mind. QFD is a tool to translate understanding of the VOC into the technical language of internal department functions. We must know enough about what the client or other stakeholder needs, expects, or desires to design an effective program process to satisfy those needs. Measurements quantify this understanding and allow effective communication as the strategic management process moves from the Macro systems view into the Meso systems level of allocating internal resources and capabilities to the development processes, as described in Chapter 3, "An Integrated QI Approach: QFD and LSS Support Macro, Meso, Micro."

As QFD activities move from function to process design, lower-level measures are required to monitor process performance. These measures must be specific enough to identify quickly when a task or output fails to meet design

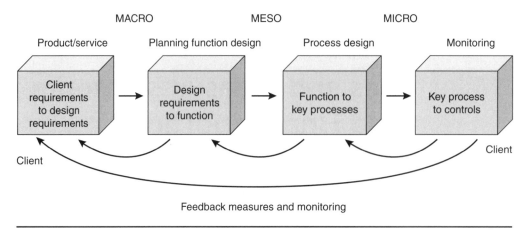

**Figure 7.1**   Client requirements to design requirements.

requirements, or when the requirement has changed enough for the process no longer to be capable of meeting new expectations. This monitoring comes in the form of milestones (time lines for assessment and feedback) established when the process steps are designed and tasks assigned. Then, as the service or program is implemented, milestone measurements give timely indication of whether the service is meeting the outcomes intended. The feedback arrows in Figure 7.1 show that measures provide immediate information on the performance at each step of the design flow from program/service planning to key process controls and monitoring at the time of service delivery.

This chapter introduces tools and techniques for measuring and monitoring at each of the Macro, Meso, Micro, and Individual levels of the continuous QI system. Texts for further study are made available in footnotes, which reference other significant resources for using milestones and measures to improve department performance.

# MEASUREMENT CHARACTERISTICS

Whether the measures are strategic and broad to support the long-term vision of the health department, or intensely granular to measure day-to-day activities, certain characteristics matter. Consistent with the concepts of QFD and LSS, measurements should be:

- Client and community focused

- Cost effective

- Consistent

- Controllable

Defining the client and community is a big part of being client and community focused. Measuring the needs and desires of the wrong client or community population in need of a program will not serve a lean, efficient operation. Chapter 4, "Customer Focus: Revitalizing Your Organization to Become Customer Centric," provides suggestions on defining and focusing on the correct customer. Many processes also have more than one customer. The QFD relationship matrix described in Chapter 13, "Navigating the Matrices," is designed intentionally to help identify customer needs and prioritize them against internal resources of the organization.

There are several ways to gather data from the customer (for health departments, the customer can be defined as a client for a service, or a community population at risk). QFD addresses the proactive search for critical to quality (CTQ) input from all affected parties of a transaction. Customer satisfaction data measures the response of the customer once they have experienced the program or service. Customer complaint ratios also are derived from customer experience with the program or service, although hopefully as a smaller subset of information. Different valuable information is gained from analyzing customer data, depending on the perspective of the study.

Figure 7.2 illustrates an example of a QFD matrix linking initial client requirements for expedited food stamps within the Florida Department of Children and Families (DCF) with design requirements. Four client requirements are shown and 10 design requirements are specified. The *client* requirements, customer quality requirements in this example, are listed on the left of the QFD matrix. The *design* requirements as listed in the columns at the top of the matrix are functions within DCF designed to provide support to the identified customer requirements. The legend at the right of the figure explains the symbols added to the core matrix for strength of the relationship between the function within DCF and its ability to address the identified customer requirement. The legend at the top left of the figure relates to the cross functional relationship between the design requirements listed along the top axis of the matrix.

Listing customer requirements in a QFD matrix provides guidance to the QI team for establishing measurements to verify that each function within the health department is meeting interim and final outcome expectations of related service processes. A major LSS tool designed to support the measurement and monitoring of process outcomes is the control plan, as shown in Figure 7.3. This control plan shows the DCF QFD matrix CTQ items from Figure 7.2 listed in the left column, with related measurement and control elements listed across the top. This control plan serves as a worksheet for the QI team to ensure that each customer requirement is carefully monitored for fulfillment and that ongoing controls are in place to make sure internal processes do not degrade.

Notice in Figure 7.2 that the recommended measures are described in simple and direct terms. There is no need to create complex measurement systems. Use

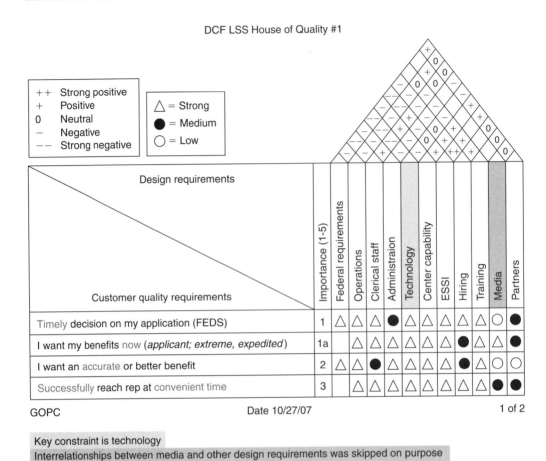

**Figure 7.2**    Florida Department of Children and Families QFD customer requirements to design requirements (partial).

existing measures with which employees are already familiar whenever appropriate and available. Many health department programs are established under the direction of state and federal programs. These programs and the funding organizations often require specific measurements. If these measures meet the needs of local data analysis, there is no reason to create new ones. The cost of collecting measurement data should not exceed the value of the indicator. The Public Health Accreditation Board[1] is working with several Public Health not-for-profit support organizations to suggest measurement conventions to support the 10 essential services[2] of an effective department. This chapter includes suggestions to establish effective process and task measures for both interim and final performance monitoring.

Measures must also be consistent with the long-term strategy of the health department. Chapter 3 describes a systems approach to aligning the Macro, Meso, Micro, and Individual levels of activities within the health department and

Control plan for Dept of Children and Families customer to design requirements QFD matrix

| Plan revision # _____ Revision date: | Meeting members: | Page # |
| Contact person: | | Date: |

| Process | Process step | Key input variable | Key output variable | Special characteristics | Measurement | Success target | Sample size for measure | Measurement frequency | Initial process performance | Control method | Reaction path | Interactions with other departments |
|---|---|---|---|---|---|---|---|---|---|---|---|---|
| Timely decision on application | Approve | Full info | Approved app. | <7 day cycle time | Cycle time | % within cycle time | Total volume | Weekly | TBD | Run chart histogram | Mgt oversight | Call center, I/T, H/R |
| Benefits NOW | | | | | | | | | | | | |
| Accurate or better benefit | | | | | | | | | | | | |
| Reach DCF rep at convenient time | | | | | | | | | | | | |
| Reach rep who speaks my language | | | | | | | | | | | | |
| Treated with care and concern | | | | | | | | | | | | |

**Figure 7.3** Control plan for DCF customer to design requirements QFD matrix.

the greater community it serves. Measures cascade from strategic, to tactical, to operational in support of the goals, objectives, tasks, and activities performed to meet client and community needs. Collecting consistent data over the life of a program or process enables long-term analysis of trends and the identification of opportunities for improvement. As mentioned in the previous paragraph, national Public Health committees are currently defining a structure of assessments and measures that will allow local leaders to compare performance against consistent data across the country.

Finally, measures must be controllable. The person performing the process being measured should have influence over what is being measured. It is not reasonable to assume that in a complex organization an individual will have control over every activity with which they are involved. It is important, however, that the measurement data collected about an activity be understood and directly related to something that the health department is able to influence or control. Worker and leader frustration often stems from being held accountable for performance when there is no ability to influence the outcome.

The primary purpose of measurement is to support *decisions:* about how things are going, whether changes are necessary, and what works best for improving performance in a particular situation. Further perspectives on control and decision making over project outcomes are provided in Chapter 11, "Developing the QFD Team."

Data are necessary for deciding how to manage current programs and how to design and implement future ones. The forms of measurement (such as counting accomplishments and business results over time) and analysis (such as graphs using standard charting methods) that are emphasized in Chapter 9, "The House of Lean-Six Sigma Tools and Techniques," are all aimed at supporting decisions at various levels in the department—from individual performer to senior management.

When data are collected to make decisions in an ongoing performance system, they can usually be used to assess accountability and, over time, validate the design of programs, services, and processes that support clients and the community. That is, decision-making measurement usually addresses the accountability and design validation purposes as well.

Health department leaders and managers should look at the current measurement processes and decide what types of decisions they can support. Is the measuring system simply for validation or accountability, or does it collect data that support ongoing decisions about service delivery and performance? Asking this question, regularly and seriously, will enable a manager to improve how to measure, and in some cases leads to abandoning costly but useless measurement programs and procedures.

In order for effective results to be achieved, performance management practices must be: (1) integrated into routine Public Health processes, and (2) all players within the program need to understand and be invested in his or her role within a larger system. This text identifies two successful approaches and related tools to support this systems view of quality and performance management. QFD, as seen in the example of Figure 7.2, directly ties external customer requirements to the functions, roles, and responsibilities of the organization. LSS provides a robust body of tools to maximize the organization's use of resources to meet client and stakeholder needs in the most effective and efficient way possible. The control plan shown in Figure 7.3 is a critical tool in the control phase of the evolutionary improvement DMAIC model for LSS, while it also serves as the measurement and control worksheet for the final verify phase of the DMADV redesign LSS model.

# IMPROVING PERFORMANCE IS ABOUT USING DATA

Performance management is the practice of actively using performance data to improve the public's health. This practice involves strategic use of performance measures and standards to establish performance targets and goals. Performance management practices can also be used to prioritize and allocate resources, to inform managers about needed adjustments or changes in policy or program directions to meet goals, to frame reports on the success in meeting performance goals, and to improve the quality of Public Health practice.

Performance management includes the following (see Figure 7.4) components:

1. **Performance standards:** Establishment of organizational or system performance standards, targets, and goals to improve Public Health practices

2. **Performance measures:** Development, application, and use of performance measures to assess achievement of such standards

3. **Reporting progress:** Documentation and reporting progress in meeting standards and targets and sharing this information through feedback

4. **Quality improvement:** Establishment of a program or process to manage change and achieve quality improvement in Public Health policies, programs, or infrastructure based on performance standards, measurements, and reports

The four components of performance management can be applied to:

- Human resource development

- Data and information systems

- Customer focus and satisfaction

- Financial systems

- Management practices

- Public Health capacity

- Health status

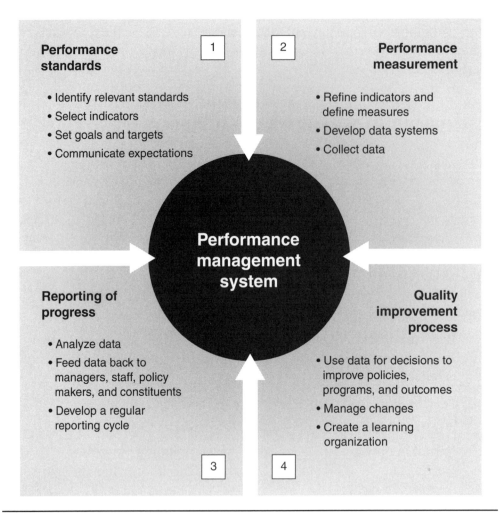

**Figure 7.4**   Performance management framework and components.

# DEFINITIONS IN SUPPORT OF PERFORMANCE MANAGEMENT

*Performance standards* are objective standards or guidelines that are used to assess an organization's performance (e.g., one epidemiologist on staff per 100,000 populations served, 80% of all clients who rate health department services "good" or "excellent"). Standards may be set based on national, state, or scientific guidelines; by benchmarking against similar organizations; based on the public's or leaders' expectations (e.g., 100% access, zero disparities); or other methods.

*Performance measures* are quantitative measures of capacities, processes, or outcomes relevant to the assessment of a performance indicator (e.g., the number of trained epidemiologists available to investigate or percentage of clients who rate health department services as "good" or "excellent").

*Performance indicators* summarize the focus (e.g., workforce capacity, customer service) of performance goals and measures, often used for communication purposes and preceding the development of specific measures.

*Performance targets* set specific and measurable goals related to agency or system performance. Where a relevant performance standard is available, the target may be the same as, exceed, or be an intermediate step toward that standard.

## EXAMPLES OF THE FOUR COMPONENTS

A performance management system is the continuous use of all the above practices so that they are integrated into an agency's core operations. Performance management can be carried out at multiple levels, including the program, organization, community, and state levels.

The Lean-Six Sigma Black Belt project undertaken in 2009 by the Orange County, FL, Department of Health Environmental Health unit is a good example of combining the four components of performance management with a recognized and effective QI model.

Figure 7.5 is an initial project flowchart of the process for approving a construction septic system permit. The project champion chose to implement a Lean-Six Sigma QI project to investigate improvement opportunities for customer satisfaction, cycle time, and cost reduction. The first project team was chartered in 2008 with the assistance of one of the authors as external Lean-Six Sigma Master Black Belt.

*Performance standards* for approving septic system permits have not yet been established by the state of Florida. Targets for cycle time, resource allocation, customer satisfaction, and audit performance are all tracked independently by the local health departments. The 2008 Environmental Health System project consisted of the Lean-Six Sigma DMAIC process to identify the current state of permitting. The 2009 project extension is identifying measures to capture process trends through the following steps.

- Define the current permit application and approval flow.

- Measure the overall cycle time from application to approval.

- Analyze data for bottlenecks, defects, and opportunities for improvement.

- Improve the existing system to better meet contractor and home owner expectations.

- Control the ongoing application and approval process to hold the improvement gains.

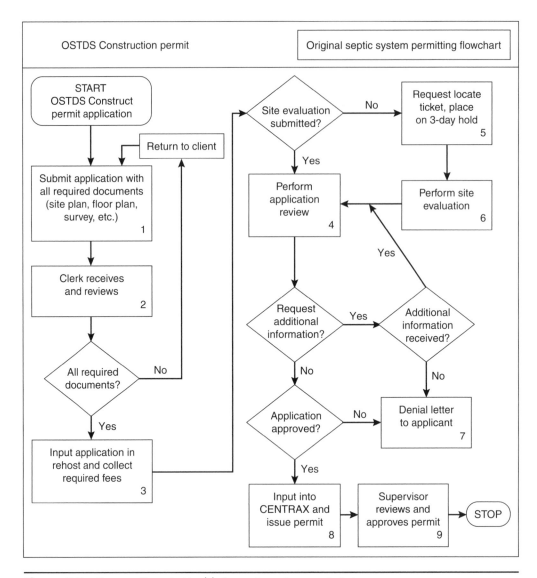

**Figure 7.5**  Orange County Health Department current state process map.

Team members from the EHV department performed time and motion studies to identify how long individual sub-processes took within each of the major process steps shown in Figure 7.5. These *performance measures* became the data for the 2008 analysis of the existing process.

The 2009 project extension is setting performance indicators chosen from among the several measurement items tracked in the 2008 performance measure step to establish a reliable database for eventual trend analysis for long-term performance expectations. These indicators, person hours, supplies, and equipment required, are collected on the flowchart summary form as shown in Figure 7.6. Person hours are tracked both by time and using average hourly pay rates.

| Flow chart step number | Meas unit | 2 | 3 | 4 | 6 | 8 | 9 | Expected | Actual | Delta |
|---|---|---|---|---|---|---|---|---|---|---|
| Type of step | | P | R | R/P | P/T | S | W | | | |
| **Cost** | | | | | | | | | | |
| • Person hours | $ | $66.43 | $12.18 | $0.18 | $0.00 | $1.76 | $3.87 | | $84.42 | |
| • Supplies required | $ | $.13 | $0.00 | $0.00 | $0.00 | $1.51 | N/A | | $1.64 | |
| • Equipment required | $ | $24.73 | 0.00 | $0.00 | $0.00 | $0.22 | 0.00 | | $24.95 | |
| **Total cost of steps** | | $91.29 | $12.18 | $0.18 | $0.00 | $3.49 | $3.87 | | $111.01 | |
| Space required (fixed, NA) | | $6.00 | N/A | N/A | N/A | N/A | N/A | | $6.00 | |
| Time | Min | 233 min | 37.40 min | N/A | N/A | 10 min | 16 min | | 296.40 min | |
| Cost of quality** • Prevention • Appraisal • Failure • Internal • External | | $66.43 $12.00 $8,000 $111.01 $8,000 | | | | | | | | |
| Partnerships needed | (NA) | Site evaluation by contractor, Property Appraiser, Sunshine line Locate, Building Department | | | | | | | | |

**Cost of quality categories are described in Chapter 6, "Using the Language of Senior Management—The Bottom Line"

Step type legend: P = Process, D = Decision, T = Transport, W = Wait, S = Storage, R = Review

**Figure 7.6**   Flowchart summary form for septic system permitting QI project.

The *reporting of progress* with local improvement efforts was the goal of the initial 2008 QI project. The second LSS Black Belt project was chartered in summer 2009 to further improve resource utilization and customer satisfaction with the approval of new septic system permits.

Short-term *performance targets* were established during the summer 2009 LSS project through discussion with the subject matter experts within EVH. Clerical staff observed cycle time for individual process steps and established an average actual time for their efforts. Site inspectors analyzed their processes and contributed an average cycle time for application review, soil testing, and site inspection activities, while team leaders and supervisors estimated the time for review and approval steps. These local targets are reflected in the flowchart summary form as the Actual column to the right of the form. Interim local expected values are being set to complete the flowchart summary form and allow for a delta analysis. Once this delta is understood, the Lean-Six Sigma QI team will identify *quality improvement process* targets.

Current activities are focused on internal process improvement and stability. The intent is to provide a consistent, accurate, and timely septic system permitting process and thereby increase the satisfaction of the external customers of this county health department service. Customer satisfaction is not tracked on the flowchart summary form in this interim project. That is planned for future iterations of this team mandate.

## DOES YOUR AGENCY HAVE A PERFORMANCE MANAGEMENT SYSTEM?

There are a series of questions the Public Health Foundation has identified to assist Public Health leadership in assessing their effectiveness using the turning point performance management system.[3] The following questions are strongly related to a quality and performance excellence culture at the organizational level:

- Do you set specific performance standards, targets, or goals for your organization? How do you determine these standards? Do you benchmark against similar state organizations or use national, state, or scientific guidelines?

- Do you have a way to measure the capacity, process, or outcomes of established performance standards and targets? What tools do you use to assist in these efforts?

- Do you document or report your organization's progress? Do you make this information regularly available to managers, staff, and others?

- Do you have a quality improvement process? What do you do with the information gathered in your progress report or document? Do you have a process to manage changes in policies, programs, or infrastructure that are based on performance standards, measurements, and reports?

A successful performance management system is driven by state and local needs and designed to closely align with a Public Health agency's mission and strategic plans. Public Health agencies have applied the four components in a variety of ways.

## PERFORMANCE MEASURES

To select specific performance measures, Public Health agencies may consult national tools containing tested measures, such as Tracking Healthy People 2010,[4] as well as develop their own procedures to help them assess performance. The state of Washington performs field tests with state and local health departments to determine how well its measures work for evaluation. Texas created an intranet reporting system for its agency users, which helped increase efficiency and accuracy of reporting on its performance measures. The Texas Performance Measure Management Group meets quarterly to discuss measures and reporting. Because quantitative data sometimes are not available to measure performance indicators, New Hampshire includes a provision in its performance-based contracting system requiring contractors to describe activities for which they cannot provide data to assess their performance. Contractors are advised to develop systems to capture the data needed for the performance measures.

## REPORTING OF PROGRESS

How a Public Health agency tracks and reports progress depends upon the purposes of its performance management system and the intended users of performance data. In Ohio, the Department of Health publishes periodic reports on key measures (identified by department staff), which are used by the agency for making improvements. Relevant state and national performance indicators are reviewed by representatives of all interested parties. Casting a wider net for reporting and accountability, Virginia established a Web site to make performance reports and planning information accessible to policy makers, Public Health partners, agency employees, and citizens.

Saginaw County, Michigan, uses the results of its MAPP-based community-wide assessments to enhance the measures consistently gathered through their

---

**Pennsylvania Department of Health**

**DATA DRIVEN MANAGEMENT PROGRAM**

*Welcome to the PADOH Data Driven Management Program (DDM) Intranet site.*

**Our Vision** is that all PaDOH programs/operations manage and improve performance and quality to get better results.

**Our Mission** is to develop, identify, evaluate, and help PaDOH programs/operations implement promising and proven performance management techniques to benefit the public's health.

The **Program Evaluation Section** is located in the Bureau of Health Statistics and Research Division of Statistical Support.

The **DDM Steering Council** was established to develop and implement DDM strategy and initiatives.

---

**Figure 7.7**    Introduction to the Pennsylvania Department of Health Intranet site for data driven management.

partnership with the University of Michigan and national Public Health data sources.[5] The Pennsylvania Department of Health uses the PHF turning point model as the basis for its data-driven management approach to continuous improvement.[6] Pennsylvania is benchmarking with the city of Austin, TX, which is also using a data driven management approach to performance assessment and improvement.[7] Figure 7.7 is a copy of the mission, vision, and structure of the performance management system being developed by the Pennsylvania Department of Health in Harrisburg. This integrated performance management system is designed to work in parallel with the data gathered during QI activities across the health department. The Public Health Foundation provided a series of educational sessions and facilitated process improvement workshops in 2007 and 2008 in support of the Pennsylvania initiative.

## THE PERFORMANCE MANAGEMENT CYCLE

The ideas of "continuous quality improvement" and a cycle of "performance-based management" are not new. In the 1950s, W. Edwards Deming, well-known quality guru and management consultant, transformed traditional industrial thinking about quality control with his emphasis on employee empowerment, performance feedback, and measurement-based management. Deming believed the following:

- Inspection measures at the end of a production line ignore the root causes of defects and result in inefficiencies. Discarding defective products creates more waste than "doing it right the first time."

- Defects can be avoided and quality improved indefinitely if these root causes are discovered and addressed through ongoing evaluation processes. Companies should adopt a cycle of continuous product and process improvement, often referred to as "Plan-Do-Check-Act."

- All business processes should be part of an ongoing measurement process with feedback loops. Managers, working with employees, should examine data fed back to them to determine causes of variation or defects, pinpoint problems with processes, and focus attention on improving specific aspects of production.[8]

Many subsequent models, such as Total Quality Management in the 1980s, take root in Deming's philosophy. This text describes a more recent model, the Lean-Six Sigma approach.

In Public Health, the "production line" to create healthy communities has many aspects that must continually be managed with feedback loops, as described in Chapter 1, "The Continuum of Quality Improvement in Public Health."

Although those working in Public Health are mission-driven with a focus on health outcomes, checking only health status and other outcomes will not help to identify root causes of health problems or inefficiencies. To create high-performing agencies, the efficiency and quality of related inputs and outputs leading to better outcomes must be managed.

An optimal Public Health performance management approach creates feedback loops around the following three aspects:

1. Structures such as financial and information resources

2. Processes such as health promotion and epidemiology services

3. Outcomes such as health status and cost savings

For an illustration of a continuous performance feedback loop involving structural capacity, processes, and outcomes related to Public Health, refer to the performance measurement model in Figure 7.8.[9]

The reader will notice in Figure 7.8 the reference to the Macro context driving the local Public Health system (PHS) mission and purpose. This translation of the Macro drivers for system outcomes into a local configuration becomes the Meso level of shorter cycle strategic planning (18–36 months) and tactical applications for structural capacity. The Micro and Individual levels of the continuum of quality improvement are designed around the 10 essential Public Health services, which provide a flexible yet consistent framework for community focused outcomes.

In the model described in Figure 7.8, the Macro, or community, context of Public Health translates into an integrated system of structural capacity and

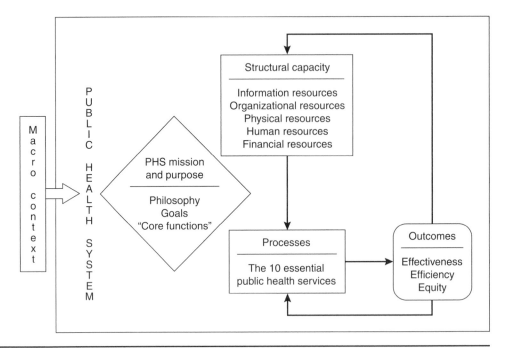

**Figure 7.8**    Conceptual framework of the Public Health system as a basis for measuring the Public Health system's performance.

process guided by the Public Health system mission and purpose. This integrated system drives the effectiveness, efficiency, and equity of the outcomes of the local Public Health system.

## PROCESS MEASURES IN MESO TO MICRO LEVEL DEPARTMENT ACTIVITIES

Here are some things to keep in mind when assigning measures to processes:

- Don't confuse process measures and functional measures. Cross-functional processes require cross-functional measures.

- Processes produce outputs for stakeholders. Measure the degree to which the process meets stakeholder requirements.

- Someone needs to be accountable for process performance. Create a measurement-friendly culture in which such accountability is an accepted part of day-to-day operations.

- Build credibility into the performance measures. Remove opportunities for anyone to challenge the need for change based on poor performance measurements.

- Design the measurement methods as well as the measures. Where will the data come from? Who will do the analysis? How will the information be reported? Can the cost of collection, analysis, and reporting be justified?

- Look to measure things that go wrong. The purpose of measurement is to track performance. We should be more interested in things that go wrong than in things that go right.

- Don't just map your existing measures onto new definitions of process. If the process modeling and analysis is new, then it is unlikely that your existing measures will be a complete set of process measures.

- Be serious about process performance measurement. Know why you are measuring and what decision you will make from analysis of the data![10]

Measurement and performance improvement using quantitative data is an emerging initiative within local Public Health departments and municipal governments. The tools of performance management, paired with the concepts of QFD and Lean-Six Sigma can be effectively applied to this strongly service-based environment. By identifying the critical customer requirements for a process and establishing realistic and effective measures to the attainment of these requirements, health departments can create a strong foundation for continuous improvement.

# ENDNOTES

1. For more information about the Public Health Accreditation Board, go to http://www .phaboard.org (accessed September 9, 2009).
2. L. C. Corso and P. J. Wiesner, "Using the Essential Services as a Foundation for Performance Measurement and Assessment of Local Public Health Systems," *JPHMP,* 6(5) (2000): 1–18.
3. Turning Point: From Silos to Systems, http://www.phf.org/pmqi/silossystems.pdf, *Public Health Foundation* (accessed June 5, 2009).
4. U.S. Department of Health and Human Services, http://www.healthypeople.gov/Document/ (accessed November 11, 2009).
5. R. Bialek, G. Duffy, and J. Moran, eds., *The Public Health Quality Improvement Handbook* (Milwaukee, WI: Quality Press, 2009), Chapter 10.
6. Agenda for Data Driven Management Training by the Public Health Foundation, February 2008, hosted by C. Berger and P. Zitzer, http://www.phf.org/infrastructure/paagenda. pdf; additional DDM newsletters and monographs available through the Pennsylvania Department of Health intranet site (accessed November 13, 2009).
7. Austin City Connection, http://www.ci.austin.tx.us/budget/eperf/index.cfm (accessed November 13, 2009).

8. W.E. Deming, *Out of the Crisis* (Cambridge: Massachusetts Institute of Technology, 1982).

9. A. Handler, M. Issel, and B. Turnock, "A Conceptual Framework to Measure Performance of the Public Health System," *American Journal of Public Health,* 91 (2001): 1235–1239.

10. R. Tregear, The Problem of the Question Mark, www.BPTrends.com (accessed September, 2009).

# 8

# Lean-Six Sigma:
# "Faster, Better, Smarter"

Lean-Six Sigma (LSS) is a methodology that integrates two QI models: lean and Six Sigma methodologies. Health departments can use LSS to eliminate waste and reduce delivery time for services to meet the ever faster response times expected by clients, communities, and government officials. Unless all available resources are directly engaged in the fulfillment of a customer need, something is being wasted. Public Health department leaders can use lean and Six Sigma to meet the needs of the community faster, better, and smarter than we have in the past.

Michael George, in *Lean Six Sigma for Service,*[1] identifies the major areas of emphasis common to the separate disciplines of lean and Six Sigma, which have been combined into the Lean-Six Sigma methodologies:

- Systemwide integration

- Leadership involvement and visibility

- Business process focus

- Voice of the customer driven

- Change management oriented

- Project management dependent

Lean-Six Sigma builds on the practical lessons learned from previous eras of operational improvement. The early QI activities began in Japan with the work of Joseph Juran and Edwards Deming in the 1950s. Subsequent development of improvement models occurred in the 1960s and '70s with the Toyota production system (TPS) (also in Japan), spawning a resurgence of quality systems development in the expansive economic years of the 1980s. The Japanese TPS migrated to the United States with just-in-time (JIT) concepts of kanban (pull systems) and other precursors of lean manufacturing. Total quality management

(TQM) grew out of a desire to expand the World War II–era quality control and assurance activities throughout the entire organization. Team-based quality approaches, such as quality circles followed Kaoru Ishikawa's book, *What Is Total Quality Control?*,[2] to the West at the same time the international business community was embracing the standardization of quality methods by transitioning the U.S. military production standards to what is now known as the International Organization for Standards standards.[3]

The concept of Six Sigma was developed in the 1980s at Motorola as an approach to reducing variation in production processes.[4] The primary metric of Six Sigma is the defect per million opportunities (DPMO). Six Sigma is a mathematical term that refers to 3 defects per million. In Six Sigma, the higher the sigma level the better the process output which translates into fewer errors, lower operating costs, lower risks, improved performance, and better use of resources. General Electric followed the Six Sigma path in the 1990s, followed by numerous businesses which embraced the terminology of Six Sigma as preferred customer-oriented management philosophy.

Quality professionals recently recognized the benefits of combining the waste reduction features of lean and the customer–focused value of Six Sigma. As seen in Figure 8.1, by the late 1990s and into the 21st century, Lean-Six Sigma had become an accepted model for organizational performance improvement and business process management.

A key phrase in the LSS model is "faster, better, smarter." An earlier phrase, "faster, better, cheaper," was modified to recognize that cheaper is not always the best approach. Wise use of resources to meet critical needs is smart. Reducing costs and expenses beyond the organization's ability to recover from an unexpected occurrence (cheaper) often causes more waste than dedicating the correct amount to begin with. In transforming Public Health departments to an LSS organization, these three elements are critical for long-term success. Remember, LSS is not a destination; once started, it is a never-ending journey. If we take our eye off the target or forget to monitor and continuously improve processes, the gains already made will be lost. The goal for leaders in Public Health is to always seek a faster, better, or smarter way to meet the needs of the community.

Many begin the quality improvement journey in Public Health through the plan-do-check-act (PDCA) process. LSS is a detailed PDCA process that relies on a more comprehensive set of milestones and measures. LSS has a robust set of steps that guide the QI team from the first awareness of an opportunity for improvement, through the design, development, implementation, and maintenance of a new level of performance.

LSS is a recommended QI model because it is "clean and neat." LSS has terms to identify baby steps for improvement, or big visions for breakthrough. LSS is similar to TQM, continuous quality improvement, and business process

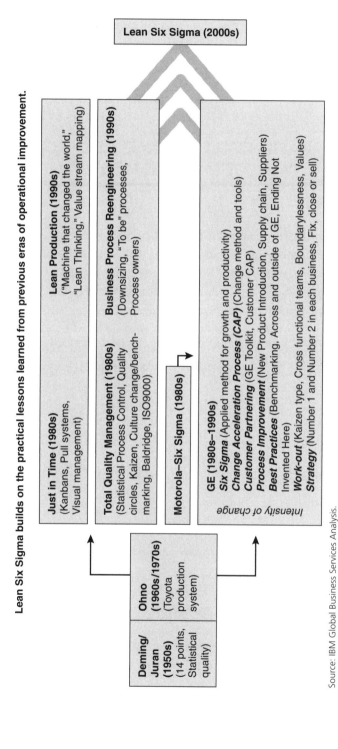

Source: IBM Global Business Services Analysis.

**Figure 8.1** Evolution of Lean-Six Sigma methodologies.

management. The terminology has been updated to reflect additional behavioral and business performance research performed over the past 20 years.

LSS provides a common language around which to discuss quality improvement. Knowing the language of improvement is important in order to communicate on the same wave length and to get things done "faster, better, smarter." Mapping the six major areas of emphasis for LSS to the concept of "faster, better, smarter" provides a useful platform for applying LSS to Public Health.

## RAPID CYCLE CHANGE AND PROJECT MANAGEMENT

### Faster

Faster, in itself, is *not* better. Faster while meeting the needs of the customer and using resources responsibly helps get more of the right tasks done at the right time and for the right reasons. Rapid cycle change and rapid cycle improvement are closely related in a LSS culture. A useful model for sequencing activities for rapid cycle change or improvement is:

**R**ealization of a problem or issue that needs to be corrected

**A**ct to start a resolution or change to the problem or issue that needs to be corrected

**P**lan for success

**I**nvolve key constituents

**D**evelop the change team and establish the rapid cycle time line

**C**onsultative training interventions

Anal**Y**ze baseline data

**C**onstruct solutions

**L**aunch pilot improvement plan

**E**valuate results achieved from pilot improvement

The **R**ealization of an issue, **P**lanning for success, **I**nvolving key constituents, and **D**eveloping the change team are all part of the Plan part of PDCA cycle. The **C**onsultative training interventions, anal**Y**ze baseline data, and **C**onstruct solutions are in the Do part of PDCA cycle. The **L**aunch pilot improvement plan is the Check part of the PDCA cycle. The **E**valuate results achieved from pilot improvement are the Act part of the PDCA cycle when the QI team assesses whether the changes have improved the process and are meeting customer requirements. If requirements are met, the changes are documented and integrated into daily management and operations. If the requirements are still not met after the implementation of the rapid cycle PDCA process, identify the gaps in performance, engage in root cause analysis, and go through the cycle again for increased performance.[5]

## Lean-Six Sigma Requires Effective Change Management

Successful organizational improvement depends upon a well-planned and robust implementation of change management. Health departments are transforming themselves to meet increasing rates of change in legislation, requirements from funding bodies, and expectations from the multitude of community segments that are served.

Transformation means change. Change in the right direction is improvement. In other words, change does not necessarily result in improvement, but all improvement requires change. The transition from business as usual to LSS model is sometimes difficult for employees because it involves change. LSS uses techniques for both incremental, never-ending improvements as well as break-through improvements (see Chapter 10, "Incremental Versus Redesign Strategies"), which means the LSS journey encounters both gradual as well as fast-paced changes.

A key perspective of transformational change is that of "saturation and repetition." Change management is a process like any other process, although it may be more complex than most. *Saturation* refers to the proportion of a health department staff that becomes involved in QI methods and improvement projects. *Repetition* refers to the number of times a specific staff member becomes involved in a QI project. Participants in the change process learn more quickly and become comfortable with the idea of change through saturation and repetition. The more a new task is performed, the more comfortable staff become with the process and the outcomes of that function. The term "saturation marketing" may be familiar to the reader. Saturation marketing is experienced on a television station when each commercial break shows the same advertisement over and over again. Saturation in the context of change management means being so immersed in the subject of the change that the new task becomes a habit.

We are what we do. We are more of what we do more often. Working with LSS tools or other tools of quality improvement become easier the more frequently they are used by health department staff.[6]

Change means getting outside of a comfort zone, which is scary for many people. Management should factor this into the planning and implementation phases. There should be constant and open channels of communication regarding the need for change in today´s changing health system and the necessity of aligning department and personal goals; the message should be consistent and clear. The use of internal change agents and external change facilitators should be considered.

In the LSS transformation, as in other major change initiatives, immediate results from pilot projects get better staff buy-in. Use LSS champion(s) as mentors or coaches. (Chapter 11 addresses how to develop the QFD and LSS team.) The role of the LSS champion is critical in creating and sustaining an environment for successful change. The major elements of LSS introduced in this chapter do not stand alone. Each of the six elements overlaps the others in a system that creates an effective infrastructure for overall strategic and operational health department success. Systemwide integration stresses the importance of horizontal communication and cross-functional project orientation to better align resources to the right places at the right time.

Six LSS implementation success factors include: (1) preparing and motivating staff, (2) involving and empowering employees in the change process, (3) managing expectations (such as fear of loss of jobs), (4) fostering an atmosphere of experimentation during the transition from traditional management to LSS, (5) incorporating rewards and recognition systems, and (6) visible commitment from management.

### Project Management Dependent

A workforce that is knowledgeable about LSS tools and techniques is essential to working faster. LSS application workshops are invaluable for just-in-time adult learning and should be given just before starting a team on their improvement journey. Human development is the key in LSS deployment. Technical tools (the house of LSS building blocks) as well as physical tools (such as automation, team skills, proper equipment use and maintenance, etc.) assist in the facilitation of the humans in starting and maintaining a strong improvement culture.

A "teach-do" cycle involves immediately applying a new skill. What the individual is taught is immediately applied. Start by providing LSS training to a critical mass of employees. The LSS leader normally facilitates the training using internal and external resources. The training includes an explanation of the need for LSS and the philosophical concepts behind LSS (such as customer focus, continuous improvement, teamwork, and standardization).

## Better

### Systemwide Integration

Successful implementation of LSS depends on the total commitment of everyone every day to make it work; this means every person at all levels of the health department. All barriers walling off functions or units from each other should be removed. A systematic well-thought-out approach in a LSS transformation is the key to success. LSS recognizes the interdependence of one activity within the system with a multitude of other requirements. No process works in a vacuum. What happens in one area of the health department impacts and is impacted by other functions.

### Leadership Involvement and Visibility

Health department leadership must be involved visibly in validating the benefit of improvement to the client and the community, ensuring the strategic linkage from vision to the project or program. Senior management support is a critical component to change agent success. The adage of "what gets measured, gets managed" is true. When senior management is openly interested and concerned about the outcomes of an activity, staff are motivated to accomplish the intended outcomes. Without visible, hands-on leadership commitment and sufficient resources, team members can become demoralized. A well-planned LSS implementation strategy aligns health department goals with individual/team goals.

LSS needs to be adopted in its entirety, not piecemeal. A master plan for implementation is critical with senior managers "walking the talk." Flavor-of-the-month programs should be avoided completely. Constant top-down and bottom-up communication during the change is absolutely necessary. Senior management is responsible to help others clearly understand the need for the LSS transformation. Deming taught that 94% of control is in hands of the leadership, staff can control only 6%.[7] Management should focus attention on developing and sustaining a sense of trust, teamwork, and involving people working in the process in all LSS efforts. Equal and fair treatment of employees, data-driven decision making, and strategic thinking rather than managing for the short-term bottom-line results are extremely important.

## Smarter

### Business Process Focus

Lean addresses the efficiency of organizational functions while Six Sigma focuses on reducing variation in a process. Six Sigma is an improvement methodology that facilitates near perfection in the processes of an organization. It considers not only the average performance but also the variability of what the business presents to the customer. This variation is often the cause of the "hidden factory" or the penalty for not getting it right the first time.

The "hidden factory" is not so hidden in most Public Health offices, which can work in close quarters. The extra steps, extra time, and extra effort often put into a task can be identified relatively easily. In terms of Public Health activities, the "factory" may consist of rework costs to reprocess forms before delivery to the client, staff salary costs for time taken to correct mistakes, recovery from a poor client experience, long waits for decisions to be made, and community outcome metrics that take longer to improve. LSS methods evolve around the impact from defects in a process. In Public Health a defect can be defined as anything that results in either internal or external customer dissatisfaction.

## Voice of the Customer Driven

QFD and LSS come together most effectively when considering the voice of the customer (VOC). Figure 8.2 shows the four major quality function deployment (QFD) matrices that guide a QI team from the initial VOC and critical to quality identification through the design, development, and operational controls for effective production of products and services.

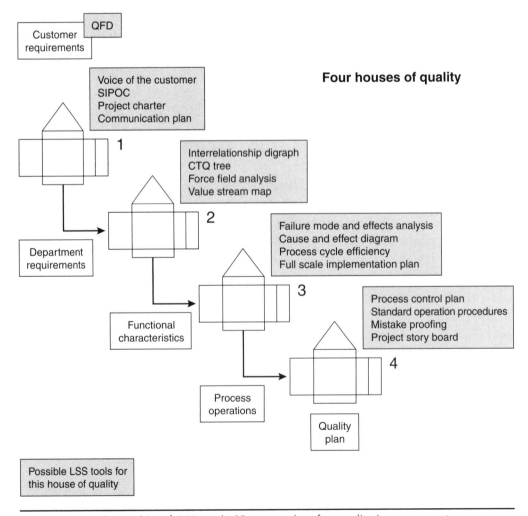

**Figure 8.2** Relationship of QFD and LSS approaches for quality improvement.

The first matrix of the QFD deals with translating of customer requirements into internal department requirements and consists of four components. The VOC and supplier-input-process-output-customer (SIPOC) are used to identify requirements and overall process flows. A *project charter* is put in place to set firm expectations for management and the project team regarding project objectives and final outcomes. A *communication plan* is developed to ensure that information and data flow to the right people at the right time and in the right amount.

The second matrix in the QFD describes the categorization of department requirements into functions as performed by the internal staff and external partners of the health department. Four components of this matrix include an *interrelationship digraph* and *value stream map* to analyze the relationships, paths of influence, and priority activities that must be undertaken to design the right processes to provide service to the client. The *critical to quality tree* (CTQ) tool helps guide discussion toward an inclusive list of the most important needs of the targeted community segment while a *force field analysis* tool helps leadership minimize barriers to implementation.

The third QFD matrix defines process operations. Once the overall functions required by the department are understood, processes identified from the second matrix are validated at the activity level. A *failure mode and effects analysis* (FMEA) and *cause and effect diagrams* are two useful techniques to identify priority areas for root cause analysis to minimize defects. *Process cycles* are studied to remove all wasted time and resources. Finally, a *full implementation plan* is developed so the process can be documented completely and workers trained for delivering the service to the recipient.

The fourth matrix of the QFD in Figure 8.2 represents the documentation and control phase of the LSS project. Here a *process control plan* is used to validate ongoing measures and monitoring efforts for long-term control of the process outcomes. *Standard operating procedures* and *department policies* are written and distributed. Front-line employees are encouraged to find ways to *mistake-proof* each process. Some common mistake-proofing techniques include visual controls and lock-step worksheets. Finally, the team completes the project documentation by creating a *storyboard* to celebrate the successful improvement journey and outcomes.

## COMBINING LEAN AND SIX SIGMA METHODS AND BENEFITS

It was mentioned in the beginning of this chapter that the concepts of lean and Six Sigma can strongly complement each other in a health department. Lean applications help reduce waste and improve flow, while Six Sigma brings a client-focused orientation to increase the health department reputation in the community it serves.

# THE DMAIC METHODOLOGY

Teams use the DMAIC methodology to identify and eliminate the causes of defects through the following planning and implementation phases of an improvement project. The acronym is defined as:

D: Define a problem or improvement opportunity

M: Measure process performance

A: Analyze the process to determine the root causes of poor performance; determine whether the process can be improved or should be redesigned

I: Improve the process by attacking root causes

C: Control the improved process to hold the gains.

Figure 8.3 provides an overview of the five primary component activities performed during each of the DMAIC steps defined below.

**Define**—Just as the name implies, this is where the defect and, moreover, the scope of the effort is determined. A project champion typically partners with a Master Black Belt (MBB) to develop the parameters of the project. They work closely to define the defect, determine the client and organizational impact, assign target dates, assign resources, and set goals for the project. This is then documented in a project charter. The project champion and MBB ensure that the project charter aligns with the health department's strategy to avoid any disconnects among the goals of the project and the organization as a whole. Once this is complete, a Black Belt can begin using QI tools (such as a process map and a cause and effect diagram) to uncover the specifics of an issue and get to the root cause of the defects. Table 8.1 describes the main responsibilities of Master Black Belts, Black Belts, and other team positions in a Lean-Six Sigma organization.

**Measure**—In this phase, the QI team determines the baseline performance of the process, validates that the measurement system in place is accurate, verifies the cost of poor quality (COPQ)—the cost of not doing it right the first time—and makes an assessment of capability. This compares the process performance level against customer expectations. In other words, how *capable* is the process in meeting my customers' needs? To give a frame of reference a process at a sigma level of 6 produces very few defects. Figure 8.4 shows that plus or minus 3 sigma (sigma means standard deviation) away from the target value under a normal bell curve produces

**The Six Sigma project DMAIC cycle**

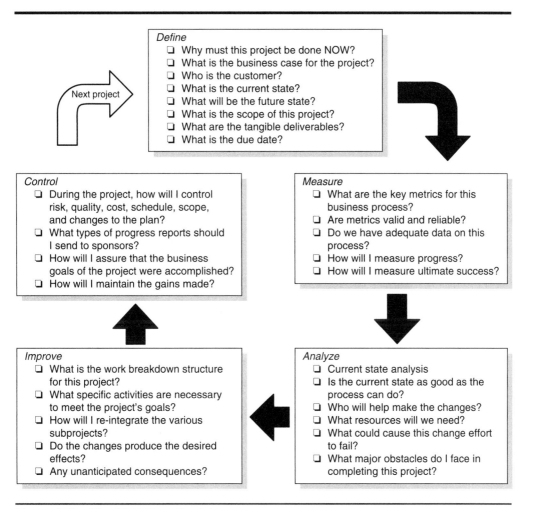

*Define*
- ❑ Why must this project be done NOW?
- ❑ What is the business case for the project?
- ❑ Who is the customer?
- ❑ What is the current state?
- ❑ What will be the future state?
- ❑ What is the scope of this project?
- ❑ What are the tangible deliverables?
- ❑ What is the due date?

Next project

*Control*
- ❑ During the project, how will I control risk, quality, cost, schedule, scope, and changes to the plan?
- ❑ What types of progress reports should I send to sponsors?
- ❑ How will I assure that the business goals of the project were accomplished?
- ❑ How will I maintain the gains made?

*Measure*
- ❑ What are the key metrics for this business process?
- ❑ Are metrics valid and reliable?
- ❑ Do we have adequate data on this process?
- ❑ How will I measure progress?
- ❑ How will I measure ultimate success?

*Improve*
- ❑ What is the work breakdown structure for this project?
- ❑ What specific activities are necessary to meet the project's goals?
- ❑ How will I re-integrate the various subprojects?
- ❑ Do the changes produce the desired effects?
- ❑ Any unanticipated consequences?

*Analyze*
- ❑ Current state analysis
- ❑ Is the current state as good as the process can do?
- ❑ Who will help make the changes?
- ❑ What resources will we need?
- ❑ What could cause this change effort to fail?
- ❑ What major obstacles do I face in completing this project?

**Figure 8.3** The DMAIC methodology.

99.9997% correct output, or 3.4 defects per million opportunities. A sigma level of one represents 690,000 defects per million opportunities. Figure 8.4 illustrates the percent nondefective within 1, 2, and 3 standard deviations from the target value.

Identifying whether the process is capable of meeting customer requirements is the first checkpoint in the measurement phase of DMAIC. Some of the tools to employ in this phase are customer surveys, complaint data analysis, Pareto charts, run charts, and control charts.

The Measure phase has 3 components: The VOC, customer requirements, and metrics. An example of the measure phase and how these three

**Table 8.1**   Lean-Six Sigma roles and responsibilities.

| Traditional Title | Public Health Title | Responsibility |
|---|---|---|
| Project champion | Same | • Dedicated to see it implemented<br>• Absolute belief it is the right thing to do<br>• Perseverance and stamina |
| Project sponsor | Same | • Believes in the concept/idea<br>• Sound business acumen<br>• Willing to take risk and responsibility for outcomes<br>• Authority to approve needed resources<br>• Upper management will listen to her or him |
| Process owner | Functional manager or unit supervisor (varies by local Public Health department) | • Is a team member<br>• Takes ownership of the project when it is complete<br>• Is responsible for maintaining the project's gains<br>• Removes barriers for Black Belts |
| Master Black Belt | Senior data analyst, quality subject matter expert, department quality manager | • Expert on Six Sigma tools and concepts<br>• Trains Black Belts and ensures proper application of methodology and tools<br>• Coaches/mentors Black and Green Belts<br>• Works high-level projects and those that impact multiple divisions or business units<br>• Assists champions and process owners with project selection, management, and Six Sigma administration |
| Black Belt | Quality tools specialist, experienced project leader, data analyst | • Leads, executes, and completes DMAIC projects<br>• Teaches team members the Six Sigma methodology and tools<br>• Assists in identifying project opportunities and refining project details and scope<br>• Reports progress to the project champions and process owners<br>• Transfers knowledge to other Black Belts and the organization<br>• Mentors Green Belts |

| | | |
|---|---|---|
| Green Belt | Team leader, project lead | • Committed to the team's mission and objectives<br>• Capable of developing process maps, applying basic quality tools, creating charts, and engaging in basic statistical analysis<br>• Experienced in planning, organizing, staffing, controlling, and directing<br>• Capable of creating and maintaining channels that enable members to do their work<br>• Capable of gaining the respect of team members; a role model<br>• Is firm, fair, and factual in dealing with a team of diverse individuals<br>• Facilitates discussion without dominating<br>• Actively listens<br>• Empowers team members to the extent possible within the organization's culture<br>• Supports all team members equally<br>• Respects each team member's individuality |
| Yellow Belt | Team member | • Willing to commit to the purpose of the team<br>• Understands lean and Six Sigma tools and concepts<br>• Able to express ideas, opinions, suggestions in a non-threatening manner<br>• Capable of listening attentively to other team members<br>• Receptive to new ideas and suggestions<br>• Able to engage in analysis of Lean-Six Sigma tools and concepts<br>• Even-tempered, able to handle stress and cope with problems openly<br>• Competent in one or more fields of expertise needed by the team<br>• Favorable performance record<br>• Willing to function as a team member and forfeit "star" status |

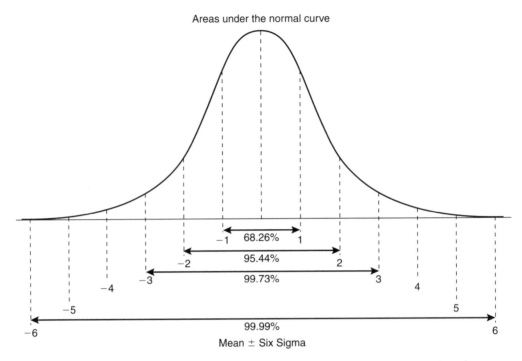

The Six Sigma level is where the performance at each function, process, or operation is nearly perfect, generating a defect rate of .000034% or only 3.4 defects per million opportunities. For comparison, a three sigma level of performance generates 66,807 defects per million opportunities.

**Figure 8.4**   Percent nondefective under a normal curve using Six Sigma concept.

components are related is shown in Figure 8.5. The example shows a consolidated call center supporting a large county health department (HD). The HD leadership met with a broad base of community stakeholders, clients, and service partners to learn of their priority needs for using the call center. It was found that prompt response time was a major external customer requirement, as identified in the statement "I consistently wait too long to speak with a call center representative."

Likewise, a significant internal customer comment was "Why are the monthly administration costs suddenly higher than the last three months?" These two statements prompted leadership to identify four measurement categories: (1) phone answer response time, (2) service satisfaction, (3) utilization efficiency rate, and (4) cost per call. The flow of the performance measure development in Figure 8.5 goes from left to right, starting with the voice of the customer into a separation of internal and external customer requirements, which are then characterized by the four measurement attributes (timeliness, responsiveness, resources, and expense).

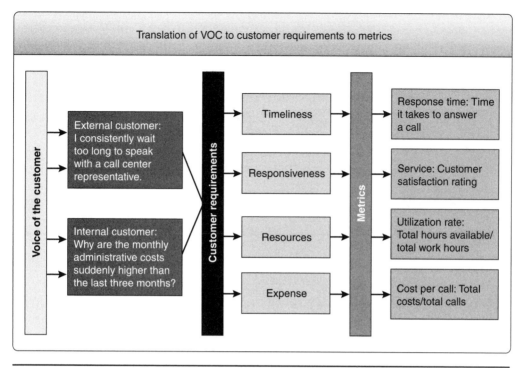

**Figure 8.5**   Performance metrics developed from customer requirements.

Metrics were then identified to support and monitor performance of each of the attributes within the department.

**Analyze**—This is the phase where the Black Belt technical expert analyzes data collected to uncover the root cause(s) of the defect. Once a QI team has isolated the potential factors hypothesis testing is done to confirm that the factor is indeed causing or contributing to the problem. Graphical analysis is typically done in this phase before any statistical testing is undertaken and questions any analysis that does not have the statistical analysis backing it up.

**Improve**—Now that the project team knows what is causing the problem, the next phase is to predict what the performance of the process would be if the identified issues are fixed. This is achieved through a number of different approaches for identifying possible solutions. The turning point Public Health foundation data management model described in Chapter 7 "Milestones and Measures; Interim and Final Reporting" is one such approach. Setting performance expectations is crucial in order to evaluate alternative solutions. Proposed solutions can be analyzed with a decision matrix using side-by-side comparisons. This step is also an opportunity for a process champion to halt the project prior to further investment and incurring greater cost. Once a solution is selected by the QI team, the improvement is implemented.

**Control**—The final phase is ensuring the solution is integrated into the health department daily operation and that it truly improved the process. Common tools in this phase are control charts, dashboards, and balanced scorecards. The process owner and team leader must demand evidence that post-implementation performance is better than it was and that it is in statistical process control. This ensures that if the process performance ever deteriorates, the process owner knows when and how to react to the situation. Another important element is the standardization of the solution across other areas of the department. Once a solution is found to be effective in one location, senior management needs to ensure that the other units also implement the improvement.

LSS provides the framework to ask the right questions to achieve the desired outcome. Understanding how a defect affects a process is critical to the success with any LSS initiative. Numerous Public Health processes can be enhanced using LSS and the DMAIC methodology. This systemized approach complements current management models used by Public Health departments, or it can replace other management models.

LSS is a data-driven methodology and can cause significant demands for data collection and reporting. The use of technology to support data collection, analysis, and reporting can provide significant cost saving through automation of work processes. Expanded data technology needs are created to support projects (low-level data needs), control plans (low- and mid-level measures), and scorecards (high-level measures). Plan a way to prioritize these data needs by balancing the more strategic needs for the high-level measurements supporting the management system and the low- to mid-level needs of the DMAIC quality improvement methodology.

# SUMMARY

When deployed properly, Lean-Six Sigma creates a structure to ensure that the health department has the right resources working on activities that will meet or exceed clients and community expectations, reduce direct costs, and provide a framework for measuring and monitoring those efforts. Done correctly, Lean-Six Sigma will:

1. Create an infrastructure for managing improvement efforts and focus your resources on those efforts.

2. Ensure that those improvement efforts are aligned with your client and stakeholder needs.

3. Develop a measurement system to monitor the impact of your improvement efforts.

While Lean-Six Sigma has been focused on high-cost training, software, teams, and variation, the future belongs to low-cost just-in-time training, software, individuals, and information transactions.[8] Any systemwide methodology for organizational improvement requires continual surveillance by senior leadership. Three important areas for senior leadership to monitor for LSS are: (1) lack of resource support for the project team, (2) support for gathering data for a project, (3) failure or resistance to implement a recommended solution.

Lean-Six Sigma depends on both quantitative and qualitative data on which to make decisions affecting the issue under study. Opinions are not sufficient to justify major process or organizational change. Unless data validate the proposed change, others may resist the change. However, data alone will not motivate some to accept change and it is helpful to solicit wide representation on QI project teams. Strong teamwork, project management, consistent leadership, and ongoing data-based decision making are all characteristics of a successful Lean-Six Sigma initiative.

## ENDNOTES

1. M. L. George, *Lean Six Sigma for Service* (New York: McGraw Hill, 2003), pp. 6–9.
2. K. Ishikawa, translated by J. Lu, *What Is Total Quality Control? The Japanese Way* (Englewood Cliffs, NJ: Prentice Hall, 1985).
3. For full information on the International Organization for Standardization: http://www.iso.org/iso/home.htm (accessed November 23, 2009).
4. J. R. Evans and W. M. Lindsay, *The Management and Control of Quality,* 6th ed. (Mason, OH: Thompson/Southwestern, 2005), pp. 132–133.
5. J. W. Moran, G. L. Duffy, and W. Riley, *Rapid Cycle PDCA* (Texas Quality Foundation Update, August 2009).
6. W. Riley, H. M. Parsons, G. L. Duffy, J. W. Moran, and B. Henry, "Realizing Transformational Change Through Quality Improvement in Public Health," *Journal of Public Health Management and Practice,* 16, special ed. no. 2, (January/February 2009).
7. W. E. Deming, *Out of the Crisis* (Cambridge: Massachusetts Institute of Technology, 1986).
8. J. Defeo, "Six Sigma: Perfection *Is* Possible in Meeting Customer Needs," *2000 Handbook of Business Strategy* (New York: Faulkner & Gray, 2000).

# 9

# The House of Lean-Six Sigma Tools and Techniques

Lean-Six Sigma is not a new set of quality improvement tools. Many of the tools have been used in organizations since the 1960s and 1970s, as introduced in Chapter 8, "Lean Six Sigma: 'Faster, Better, Smarter.'"

An early improvement model used in Public Health quality improvement activities is the plan-do-check-act (PDCA) cycle. The PDCA cycle was developed by Walter Shewhart and the 1920s and popularized by W. Edwards Deming.[1] Figure 9.1 shows the iterative cycle of continuous improvement and four components: (1) plan—prepare a change, (2) do—implement a change, (3) check—study the impact of the change, (4) act—implement the change on a wider scale if it has the desired impact; if the change does not have the expected impact, then repeat the PDCA cycle. This PDCA technique is used when a process needs a change in direction . . . usually because the process output is deteriorating or customer needs have changed.

Figure 9.2 gives a more detailed picture of the general approach to process improvement. This figure includes a number of basic quality tools recommended for use at different stages of the PDCA cycle. These tools, such as brainstorming, flowcharts, cause and effect diagrams, root cause analysis, and control charts, are explained in *The Public Health Quality Improvement Handbook,* published by the authors in 2009.[2] These tools have been successfully used in business for many years and have great value in Public Health applications. A grid indicating a general plan-do-check-act cycle overlays the improvement process steps to show how the tools might support individual steps in the PDCA cycle.

The basic tools of quality improvement proved so effective that a number of more advanced tools were created. Organizations saw the value of using QI tools in the original manufacturing environment and benefited from using the concepts in administrative, service, design, and marketing processes. A robust set of advanced tools is used in QI approaches culminating in what is now known as Lean-Six Sigma. Figure 9.3 illustrates a complex, cross-functional

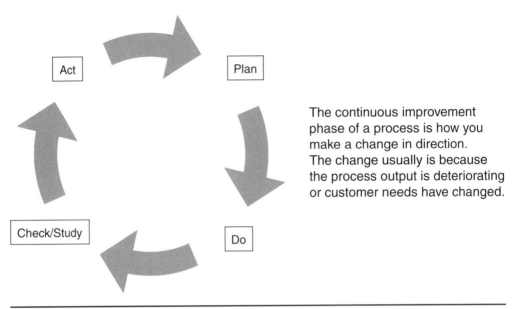

The continuous improvement phase of a process is how you make a change in direction. The change usually is because the process output is deteriorating or customer needs have changed.

**Figure 9.1**   The PDCA continuous improvement cycle.

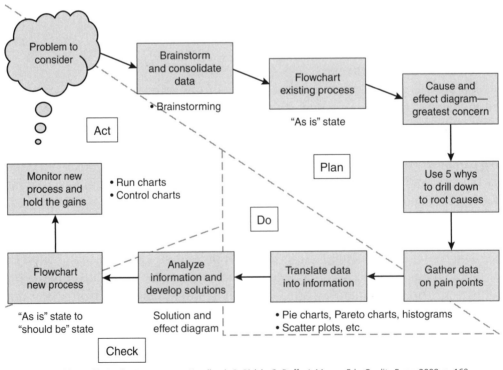

Source: *The Public Health Quality Improvement Handbook*. R. Bialek, G. Duffy, J. Moran, Eds. Quality Press, 2009, p. 160.

**Figure 9.2**   General approach using the basic tools of quality improvement.

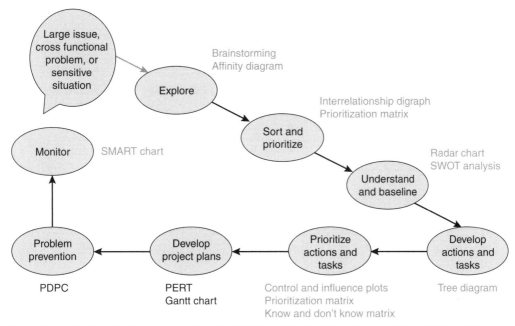

Source: *The Public Health Quality Improvement Handbook.* R. Bialek, G. Duffy, J. Moran, Eds. Quality Press, 2009, p. 160.

**Figure 9.3** General approach to using the advanced tools of quality improvement.

problem-solving process flow, including some of the more advanced project management techniques such as Gantt charts and program evaluation and review technique (PERT) charts. Although the PDCA cycle is a proven improvement model, new models such as Lean-Six Sigma (LSS) consist of more detailed guidance for performance management in more complex situations.

LSS is just a more detailed PDCA process, with five DMAIC phases (Define, Measure, Analyze, Improve, and Control) to guide the QI team through the improvement process. The robust LSS steps take a team from awareness of an opportunity for improvement, through the design, development, implementation, and maintenance of a new level of process performance.

The LSS DMAIC management system is described in more detail in Figure 9.4. Each phase is composed of a series of activities, culminating in a toll-gate review with senior management. This toll gate serves two purposes. First, it provides an opportunity for the team to focus its activities around the intended outcomes of the project. This helps to focus the vision on the bigger picture and gets our heads out of the weeds. Second, it ensures that the project sponsor and select stakeholders are updated on project progress to secure approval for moving to the next phase of improvement activities.

The tools and improvement phases of the LSS DMAIC cycle are an effective partner with quality function deployment. LSS requires the voice of the customer as obtained through QFD to identify the goal for improvement. The next section of this chapter discusses major tools of Lean-Six Sigma and suggests applications within Public Health environments.

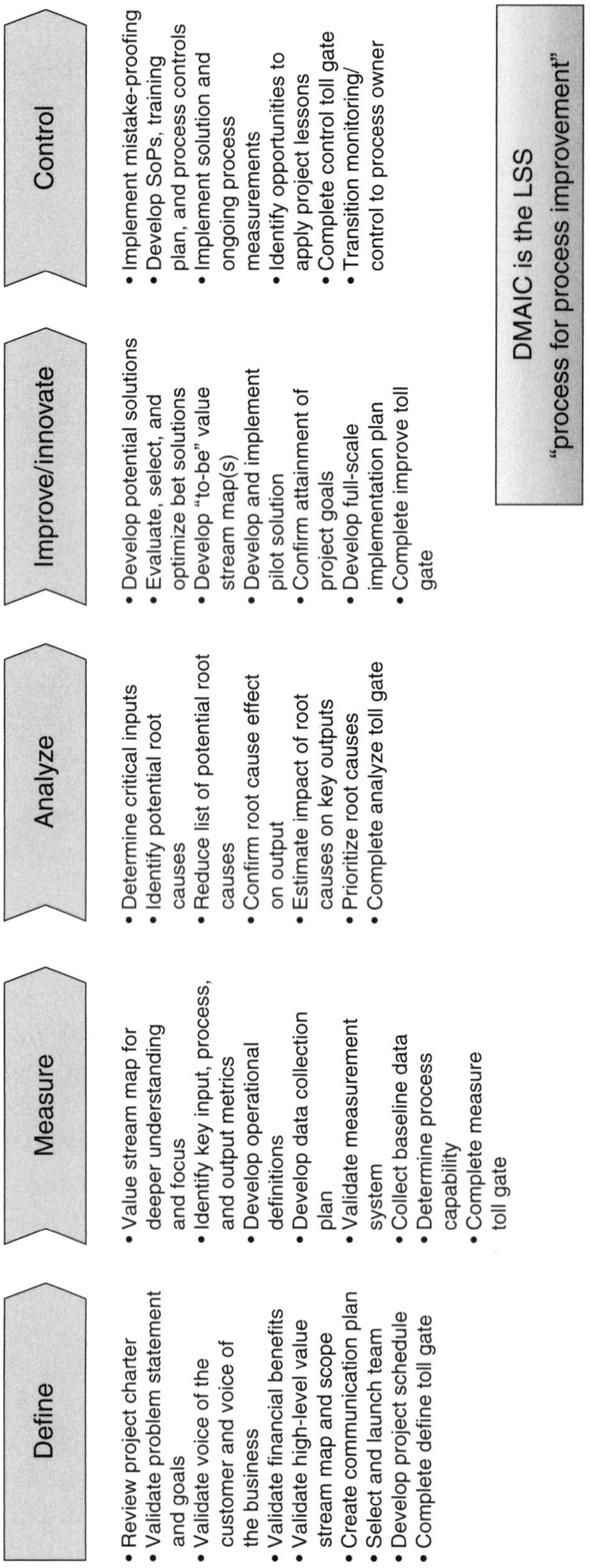

**Define**

- Review project charter
- Validate problem statement and goals
- Validate voice of the customer and voice of the business
- Validate financial benefits
- Validate high-level value stream map and scope
- Create communication plan
- Select and launch team
- Develop project schedule
- Complete define toll gate

**Measure**

- Value stream map for deeper understanding and focus
- Identify key input, process, and output metrics
- Develop operational definitions
- Develop data collection plan
- Validate measurement system
- Collect baseline data
- Determine process capability
- Complete measure toll gate

**Analyze**

- Determine critical inputs
- Identify potential root causes
- Reduce list of potential root causes
- Confirm root cause effect on output
- Estimate impact of root causes on key outputs
- Prioritize root causes
- Complete analyze toll gate

**Improve/innovate**

- Develop potential solutions
- Evaluate, select, and optimize bet solutions
- Develop "to-be" value stream map(s)
- Develop and implement pilot solution
- Confirm attainment of project goals
- Develop full-scale implementation plan
- Complete improve toll gate

**Control**

- Implement mistake-proofing
- Develop SoPs, training plan, and process controls
- Implement solution and ongoing process measurements
- Identify opportunities to apply project lessons
- Complete control toll gate
- Transition monitoring/control to process owner

DMAIC is the LSS "process for process improvement"

*Source: The Lean Six Sigma Pocket Tool Book.*

**Figure 9.4** LSS DMAIC management system.

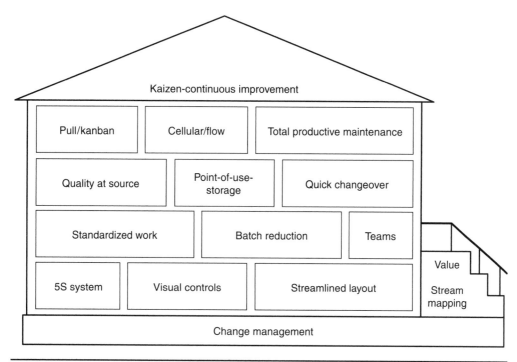

**Figure 9.5**   The House of Lean.

Figure 9.5 is a classic diagram called "The House of Lean," showing the basic tools of lean. The house consists of 12 building blocks under a roof of continuous quality improvement, based on a foundation of change management, and entered through steps of value stream mapping. A short explanation of each of the tools in the House of Lean follows.

## BUILDING BLOCKS OF HOUSE OF LEAN

The building blocks of "The House of Lean" include:

1. **The 5 Ss**: 5S is a visual method of setting the workplace in order. It is a system for workplace organization and standardization. The five steps that go into this technique all start with the letter S in Japanese (seiri, seiton, seison, seiketsu, and shitsuke). These five terms are loosely translated as sort, simplify, shine, standardize, and sustain. This is one of the most used LSS tools because it helps create a clean, orderly workplace that reduces the noise around workers (both aural and visual). See Table 9.1 for an example of the 5 Ss developed

**Table 9.1** Categories and descriptions of 5S for septic permit program.

| 5S | Description | Example |
|---|---|---|
| Sort | Distinguish needed items from unneeded items and eliminate the latter. | Identify and resolve all septic system permits on hold for additional information. |
| Simplify | Keep needed items and set them in order so they are easily accessible. | Put all active applications in green folders for easier recognition. |
| Shine | Keep the work area swept and clean. | Maintain cleanliness of front reception and waiting areas. |
| Standardize | Standardize clean-up; that is, the first three steps sort, set-in-order, and shine. | Include workforce in the documentation of process flows for all department activities. Train staff on correct procedures for all processes. |
| Sustain (self-discipline) | Make it a routine to maintain established procedures. | Institute measures at critical monitoring points for all processes. Schedule ongoing management reviews. |

for an environmental health program in a Public Health improvement project. The 5 Ss are:

**Sort** in-process applications for septic system permits.

**Simplify** all applications by placing them in "green folders" for visual recognition.

**Shine** the desks and work areas by locating all "lost" in-process applications that were causing the average turn-around time for processing to be extended.

**Standardize** the septic system permit application process by flowcharting and documenting the steps for consistency and ease of training new employees.

**Sustain** the process by including measures and review points for the office senior coordinator and first line supervisor.

2. **Visual controls:** The placement in plain view of all equipment and activities and indicators so everyone involved can understand the status of the system at a glance. Labeling of storage cabinets, closets, and other workstation resources is an example of this tool, along with diagrams of frequently performed activities for either clients or staff. This tool is often seen as a county map with major

environmental sites labeled, walk-in clinics located, or communities outlined for priority focus. Another example is the key board in the motor-pool office, indicating the availability of county, city, or state vehicles controlled by the health department.

3. **Streamlined layout:** Workplace designed according to optimum operational sequence.

4. **Standardized work:** Consistent performance of a task, according to prescribed methods, without waste, and focused on human movement (ergonomics). The spaghetti diagram prompted one local Public Health department to standardize its office flow as exhibited in Figure 9.6.

   Spaghetti diagrams are a visual representation using a continuous flow line to trace the path of a task or activity through a process. The continuous flow line enables process teams to identify redundancies in the work flow and the opportunity to expedite process flow.

   The diagram in Figure 9.6 is a spaghetti map developed for a health department administrative office. The intent of the study was to identify ways to shorten the walking time from one activity to another for frequently performed tasks. The spaghetti map shows the placement of staff and equipment in the office as well as the traffic necessary to accomplish tasks. The visual drawing highlights major intersection points within the room. Areas where many walk paths overlap are causes of delay. Waiting is one of the eight wastes of lean, as is unnecessary motion.

   The spaghetti diagram was created by a collaboration of the staff most impacted by the current workplace design. A brainstorming session was facilitated by the health department quality improvement coordinator to identify areas of congestion and wasted movement among the office personnel. Focusing on a common goal brought the team closer together, while highlighting the purpose for placement of some work areas.

5. **Batch size reduction:** Batch size consists of the number of pieces of work done at one time. The best batch size is one-piece flow, or "make one and move one." An example of how a batch size reduction was used is shown by the environmental health services department in entering applications into the database immediately upon client payment at the front desk, rather than waiting for a cluster of applications to be received before assigning numbers. Another Public Health application is the reduction of waste through printing

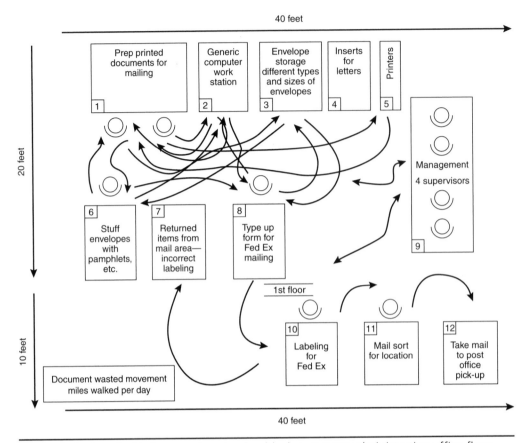

**Figure 9.6**   Spaghetti diagram showing health department administrative office flow.

smaller batches of multipart forms. Changes in grant requirements, government regulations, and department labeling were causing the staff to reprint forms frequently, making old forms obsolete. Printing fewer expensive forms at once saved budget dollars. If one-piece flow is not appropriate, reduce the batch to the smallest size possible.

6. **Teams:** In the Lean environment, the emphasis is on working in teams, whether they are (1) process improvement teams or (2) daily work teams. Lean-Six Sigma incorporates the use of teams whenever possible to provide multiple perspectives for decision making and problem solving.

7. **Quality at the source:** This consists of inspection by front-line employees so they are certain the product or service that is passed on to the next process is of acceptable quality. This approach is very useful in a local Public Health department. Since staffing is usually tight, having the skills readily available in more than one person in the office saves time and provides backup within the office.

8. **Point of use storage:** Raw material, parts, information, tools, work standards, procedures, and so forth are stored where needed. The spaghetti diagram example in Figure 9.6 is an excellent example of how one health department studied its common work area to maximize availability of supplies and work stations for effectiveness of staff within the office.

9. **Quick changeover:** The ability to change staff or equipment rapidly (usually in minutes) so multiple products in smaller batches can be run on the same equipment. This tool is translated from a production to a service environment by providing cross training of health department staff to allow quick movement from one project or client requirement to another within a small office. Another common application is the consolidation of computerized data input systems so staff does not have to take one program down and bring up another to input different forms when working with the same client.

10. **Pull:** Pull is a system of cascading production and delivery instructions from downstream to upstream activities in which the upstream supplier does not produce until the downstream customer signals a need (using a "kanban" system, named by the Japanese). The value stream mapping example shown in Figure 9.7 uses a pull system to pull supplies from the chemical treatment vendors only when the inventory reached the lowest level possible to ensure that the next task could begin without waiting on additional materials.

11. **Flow:** Physically linking and arranging manual and machine process steps into the most efficient combination to maximize value-added content while minimizing waste; the aim is single-piece flow. This is also reflected in the project that used the spaghetti diagram in Figure 9.6. The septic system permitting improvement team empowered a cross-functional group of clerical staff, inspectors, and management to create a seamless sequence of steps from client application, through processing, to permitting and final review.

12. **Total Productive Maintenance:** An equipment maintenance strategy for maximizing overall equipment effectiveness. Although the title of this tool seems complex, it is really quite simple. Every office has equipment requiring scheduled maintenance, calibration, and new release updates. A preprinted checklist or electronic reminder system for when administrative, technical, or other programmatic updates are required minimizes downtime or lack of availability of equipment when needed.

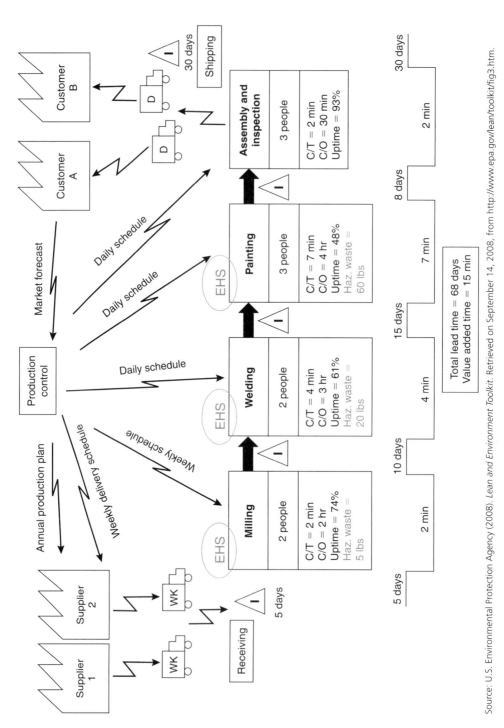

Source: U.S. Environmental Protection Agency (2008). *Lean and Environment Toolkit*. Retrieved on September 14, 2008, from http://www.epa.gov/lean/toolkit/fig3.htm.

**Figure 9.7** Current state value stream map environmental data.

# STEPS INTO THE HOUSE OF LEAN

Value stream mapping is seen as the stairway to lean because of the effectiveness of this technique in identifying opportunities for using the other tools to improve the organization as an interrelated system. The steps into the house of lean consist of a value stream map. The value stream mapping example in Figure 9.7 illustrates a use of this tool. Value stream mapping is a means of representing flow of the product or service through the process. A few of the important components of this flow include value-added activities, non-value-added activities, non-value-added but necessary activities, work in process, inventory (queues), processing time, and lead time.

Figure 9.7 is a value stream map created by a team assessing the environmental impact of a processing plant within their community. The goal is to work with the community partner not only to improve the quality of the waste water returned to the water source, but also to reduce their non-value-added activities elsewhere in the plant.

Hazardous waste is measured at each processing area in the plant. The primary purpose of the map is to focus on and reduce the amount of hazardous waste created, as well as improve the plant's disposal processes. In addition, the time between functions is measured in an attempt to use internal resources more effectively. By rebalancing workload in an efficient way, the plant management can provide more community residents with productive employment.

Non-value-added activities discovered included required management signatures when a project lead could be empowered to approve supplier orders and verify receipt of shipments. Work in process savings came from rebalancing activities between clerical and technical support staff. Clerical workers requested increased responsibilities and were rewarded for expanding their job skills. Technical staff were freed from repetitive administrative actions to focus on the backlog of chemical testing and reporting. Empowering the clerical staff by moving more tasks to a lower salary category enabled management to bring another technical professional into the organization, further reducing the backlog and adding additional skills to the team.

# THE FOUNDATION IN THE HOUSE OF LEAN

Change management is the foundation of the house of lean because all improvement comes from change. Change management works best when it comes from top leadership and flows through the entire organization. In this sense, change management is both "top down and bottom up."

## THE ROOF FOR HOUSE OF LEAN

The house of lean is covered by an overall philosophy of continuous improvement used by all managers and workers in the health department. Transformational change occurs when the management for the entire health department is done with a quality improvement perspective.

## SUMMARY

LSS is a flexible improvement model to help manage the change Public Health practitioners are introducing into the systems to improve performance. The tools described in this chapter are part of a larger set originally designed to support traditional manufacturing organizations. The tools proved so useful that industries of all sorts, from healthcare to services to not-for-profit to small business, are experiencing excellent results.

The QFD process for customer focused decision making validates the observations or opinions of those proposing change. Data alone will not motivate others to accept change. Involvement in the identification of opportunities for change and in the development of acceptable solutions is a core component of both the QFD and LSS methodologies. Strong teamwork, project management, consistent leadership, and ongoing data-based decision making are all characteristics of a successful LSS initiative.

## ENDNOTES

1. R. Bialek, G. Duffy, J. Moran, eds., *The Public Health Quality Improvement Handbook*, (Milwaukee, WI: Quality Press, 2009).
2. Ibid.

# 10

# Incremental Versus Redesign Strategies

*Parts of this chapter are based "Chapter 6: Core Process Redesign," previously published in* The Executive Guide to Improvement and Change.[1] *We have enhanced that original work to make it relevant to Public Health.*

There are two fundamental philosophies relative to improvement. Improvement may be achieved gradually, taking one small step at a time. A dramatically different concept is practiced by proponents of breakthrough improvement, a "throw out the old and start anew" approach frequently referred to as process re-engineering or process redesign. Both approaches have proven to be effective depending on the circumstances, such as the size of the organization, the degree of urgency for change, the degree of acceptability within the organization's culture, the receptivity to the relative risks involved, the ability to absorb implementation costs, and the availability of competent people to effect the change.[2] Figure 10.1 shows the incremental and breakthrough approaches.

Both incremental and breakthrough improvement focus on improving efficiency and effectiveness of processes that exist within (usually unit or program processes that use incremental improvement) and those that cut across all programs (breakthrough improvement/redesign) in the organization.

The debate over which approach is better—incremental versus breakthrough improvement—will not be solved in this chapter. Both approaches have their merits and both need to be part of any organization's active quality strategy and implementation programs. Organizations tend to do more incremental improvement because it is a place to start a quality improvement program and then grow it to a more advanced level, which will include breakthrough improvement. The people in any organization need time to develop the skills necessary for breakthrough improvement, and the tools of incremental improvement can be a foundation to build that knowledge upon.

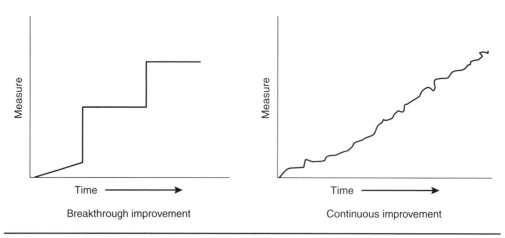

**Figure 10.1** Types of improvement.

Organizations tend to do more incremental improvement because the risks are lower, fewer people need to be involved, the impacts are local and controllable, but the cumulative effects are smaller than one large breakthrough improvement. As Hesiod, an eighth-century B.C. Greek poet, stated, "If you add a little to a little and do this often enough, soon it will become great." The problem with this approach in most organizations is a lack of patience, the ability to wait for the accumulative effect of incremental change. We want big change fast but do not understand the risks of breakthrough improvement, which is difficult to implement. It requires training and experience in redesign technology; it affects many areas, people, and processes; redesign teams tend to be large and difficult to manage; the risk of failure is high; and in a process redesign there are winners and losers, which are not present in incremental change.

Roberto Goizueta, the late CEO of Coca-Cola, stated, "If you think you are going to be successful running your business in the next 10 years the way you [did] in the last 10 years, you're out of your mind. To succeed, we have to disturb the present." But when you disturb the present, remember a quotation by former president Woodrow Wilson: "If you want to make enemies, try to change something."

The purpose of this chapter is to give an overview of the basics of a successful process redesign. Incremental improvement has been well documented in *The Public Health Quality Improvement Handbook*[3] and will not be covered here.

Core Process Redesign (CPR)[4] is a five-phase team-based methodology that helps institute a systematic process of improving how work is done in organizations. This methodology asks two key questions at each of the five phases:

1. Does the process under study support the organization's strategic mission?

2. Is the process under study necessary to meet the demands of our customer?

Process redesign is defined as "the fundamental rethinking and radical redesign of the entire business system to achieve dramatic improvements in critical measures of performance such as cost, quality, service, and speed."[5]

When a redesign team begins a CPR process, they need to keep in mind the six redesign areas shown in Figure 10.2.

The six areas of organizational redesign are as follows:

1. *Information* deals with the types of information provided by the organization to its personnel, its accessibility, and its timeliness in making decisions. Information also encompasses the critical measures the organization uses to access its performance to determine if it is successfully meeting the needs of its customers and employees. Some have narrowly defined process reengineering to be the development and deployment of sophisticated information technology (IT) systems to enhance information reporting to improve process performance. We must remember that IT is a part of most process redesigns; it is part of the solution and not the solution unto itself.

2. *Structure* looks at how the organization is organized and what the roles, responsibilities, and accountability of each area of the organization are.

3. *People* is the total human potential of the organization. This is the process of how the organization acquires, develops, and retains personnel.

4. *Rewards* focuses on how the organization formally and informally compensates its personnel for their time and effort. The reward structure must align the process with the organization's goals. There is an old saying: "What gets measured, gets done. What gets

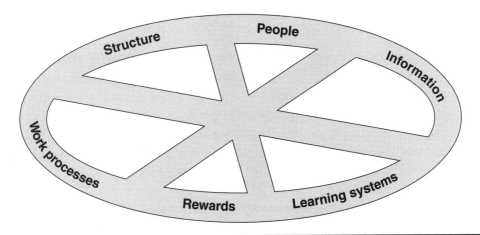

**Figure 10.2**   Six areas critical for successful business outcomes.

rewarded gets done well." Organizations need to ensure that the compensation and reward systems drive the behavior they desire.

5. *Learning systems* help improve processes because they help improve the organization's people's capabilities. These are the processes that help people acquire, transfer, and improve their knowledge base.

6. *Work processes* help the organization and its personnel focus on the concept of a process view of what it does to satisfy internal and external customers. A process view does not replace a functional view of work. The process view shows how the functional components are linked together or flow together to transfer a series of inputs into value-added outputs to customers.

When to launch a redesign effort is something every organization struggles with because it is a time- and labor-intensive process. Process redesign is also disruptive to the day-to-day operations of the organization because everyone is wondering how they will be affected in the final design. The identification of the redesign opportunities is the purview of senior management. To decide where to focus the effort requires a thorough analysis, both quantitative and qualitative. Once this analysis is completed, the data must be used to prioritize the critical processes most in need of a redesign to align them to the organization's and customers' needs. In our experience, it is necessary to redesign when:

- It becomes clear that incremental improvement will not get the organization to its goals.

- Improvement of functions or departments alone will not achieve the results desired by the organization or its customers.

- The reengineering of just one organizational system will not achieve the results desired by the organization or its customers.

Whichever processes an organization chooses to work on, redesign teams must keep in mind the strategic intent of focus of the organization (values, strategy, and goals) and the other components of the organization it may choose to redesign. When teams make a redesign choice about changing a work process, it must be in concert or aligned with these other organizational characteristics. Chapter 11 covers the basics of establishing a redesign or QFD team. The team development aspect of a redesign study is a crucial component of success and should not be taken lightly.

Conducting a redesign study requires a systematic methodology to explore and redesign work process. The core process redesign model[6] is a five-phase model, as shown in Figure 10.3.

| Phase 1:<br>Focus | Phase 2:<br>Assessment | Phase 3:<br>Negotiation | Phase 4:<br>Redesign | Phase 5:<br>Implementation |
|---|---|---|---|---|
| Form team | Map process | Identify unmet customer needs | ACT<br>• Analyze<br>• Conclude<br>• Test | Analyze implications<br><br>Seek approval |
| Focus team<br>• Mission<br>• Scope<br>• Objectives<br>• Strategic ties<br>• Measures | Assess and validate customer needs | Negotiate valid requirements<br><br>Set improvement targets and success measures | Initial change plan<br><br>Choosing the best model for your company<br><br>Mapping your PI project to the model | Refine<br><br>Monitor and measure |
| *Outcome:*<br><br>Establish the change imperative and guiding principles | *Outcome:*<br><br>Understand the current business situation | *Outcome:*<br><br>Define real requirements and gaps in performance | *Outcome:*<br><br>Develop the change plan<br><br>Pilot testing<br><br>Refinements | *Outcome:*<br><br>Dramatically improved performance |

**Figure 10.3**   The CPR pathway.

## Phase 1—Focus

The first step in an organizational redesign effort is to select those processes that have the highest potential payoff if redesigned. These are the processes with the largest gaps between performance and customer requirements or those processes most centrally linked to the success of the organizational strategy. Senior management usually undertakes this focus step as the result of an organizational assessment such as MAPP and thorough data analysis. Here they wrestle with existing strategy and goals, cost data, customer data, and staff input.

Once these high-priority processes have been chosen, the senior managers of an organization sponsor teams of employees to tackle the work of redesign. They focus organizational resources on improving the processes they have selected. In addition, as teams meet for the first time they must focus on management's requirements of their work together. To do this they must identify the scope of the proposed work (Aim statement) and document agreements with its sponsor. The process of developing and chartering a redesign teaming is discussed in detail in Chapter 11.

## Phase 2—Assessment

This is where the real work begins! Phase two of CPR starts by gathering baseline data about the organization such as strengths and weaknesses, community health status, health department system assessment, community themes, forces of change, the 10 essential services, internal surveys, process performance, and customer needs. Developing this baseline data gives the senior management and redesign team current knowledge about where the problem areas may be.

In the assessment phase we want to determine where the major performance gaps are in quality, financial, process performance, and customer needs. This will guide our decision-making process as to where we should focus our redesign efforts.

Once we have the focus area, it is important for the redesign team to map the process so everyone understands the current situation. This is an important step to do well because a good process map will show a cross-functional view of the work we are studying for a redesign. This step helps the redesign team understand how handoffs are made, the time that steps take, the costs involved, and where and how defects occur as the work under study progresses across the organization. The process map, once developed, needs to be verified by walking through the process and determining whether anything is missing or whether documented steps are not happening.

## Phase 3—Negotiation

Unlike most redesign process improvement methodologies, in which a team draws maps of the "current process," goes out and asks customers what they want, and then dives into analysis of how to make it happen, CPR spends a whole phase in the middle on "negotiation." By negotiation we do not simply mean haggling with customers, employees, or community partners but drawing them in as process partners.

Critical to an understanding of process partnership is the idea of negotiating the validity of customer, employee, and community needs. The goal of this phase is to get to a point where all parties involved in the process feel as though their concerns are being addressed, which involves discussions, joint ownership, and collaborative QI problem solving. This is where the actual redesign work starts. Chapter 4 discusses how an organization can become customer focused and outlines some methods to capture the voice of the customer and how to synthesize it into actual demands. That process is applicable to customers (internal and external), community partners, and employees as described in this section.

Because redesign may involve great changes in who does the work and how it is done, this phase concludes with a reconsideration of achievement targets and the size of the performance gap that needs to be closed. With growing pressure to reduce resources and increase productivity, it is essential that the team be very clear during phase 4 about what it is going after.

## Phase 4—Redesign

This is the phase where the team must make decisions about redesign: how the process might work better. Decisions about what to keep, what to eliminate, and what to fix are really just a series of educated guesses. They are educated guesses because they are based on the team's careful analyses of valid data; they are guesses because they are based on each member's experience, instincts, and intuition.

Many improvement methodologies and their purveyors promise they can provide magic at a certain point during the redesign effort, as though there were some sort of trick built into step X of the work. CPR offers no magic except for the natural synergy of getting the right people in the room—those who know the most about a particular work process—and providing platforms, tools, and activities that can help a team tap into its members' creativity and analytical capabilities.

In this phase of CPR, teams continue their analysis of the current work process by looking more closely at the root causes or drivers of key performance gaps and they start to explore options for closing them. This exploration entails asking a series of questions that will help the team focus on which options will give the best improvements of lower costs, reduced process time, and improved output/service quality.

The team already has many of the answers to these questions. By describing the current process, measuring its capabilities, and comparing these data with negotiated valid customer needs, it has already identified some of the shortcomings of the process. Undoubtedly, they have also started to draw conclusions about where they can change things to meet stated customer, community, and employee needs.

However, teams need to be careful about their initial conclusions. This phase involves a very basic principle, a form of scientific method: Make a hypothesis and run a scenario analysis. For every change the team proposes making in the process, it will need to look carefully at the potential consequences. For example,

- If the team takes out one step (activity, tasks, approval, handoff) to lower costs, what might happen to output/service quality? How might it impact other processes it supports?

- If they reroute the process around other steps to improve cycle time, what might happen to coordination?

- If they add steps somewhere else to increase output/service quality, what might happen to overall costs?

Every change imaginable has intended and unintended consequences. The goal as a redesign team is to find optional solutions by identifying consequences and making careful choices through "laboratory" scenario testing. The questions are endless, but the variables are not. If the team members keep their collective eyes on costs, time, and quality, they can manage the unintended consequences of change that will invariably pop up during implementation.

One tool we have found useful for CPR teams in this phase is Analyze-Conclude-Test (ACT):

- *Analyze* the work process to look for the root causes or drivers of performance gaps.

- Draw *conclusions* about what changes will close these gaps.

- *Test* your conclusions about whether you have the right improvement and whether you have gone far enough.

As noted when the team was describing the current process, analyzing processes begins the moment you get a group of people together. Even drawing a basic flowchart will reveal quick fixes and immediate improvement opportunities. Maps drawn for basic descriptive purposes are analytical and should analyze process time, costs, and rework/defect.

## Phase 5—Implementation

Once the team has proposed a new work process, it is probably eager to see it in action—to test and finalize new structures and standards for how work flows through the process. This is natural, but premature.

Successful implementation of CPR is a carefully analyzed and orchestrated process that takes into account the anticipated effects of proposed changes on the people and systems of the organization. If the team can anticipate the implications of changing the work process on such things as the competencies of the people who do the work, the information needed to get the work done, and the types of reward mechanisms needed to drive appropriate behavior, it can minimize potential failure down the road. All too often, changes that seem appropriate at one level or place in the organization wreak havoc somewhere else. To avoid fixes akin to sticking your finger in the dike while other leaks sprout, the team must step back and take a strategic view of the whole dam.

Successful implementation of CPR is an iterative process. After each step in implementation, the team must consider what modifications are needed to improve its design. Following are the steps and points of modification a team should go through before it can finalize its redesigned work process.

- Conduct a capability study and customer assessment.

- Develop an initial recommendation.

- Work with the client to finalize and implement the recommendation.

The redesign team's members must think of themselves as expert consultants hired by their organization, and the team must give the senior management team the most well-thought-out recommendations and be willing to modify its proposal to fit in with other redesign efforts to optimize the return to the organization. It is the senior management group's responsibility to consider the recommendations of multiple teams in the context of one another. Invariably there will be conflicts that must be negotiated and modifications that must be made. Remember, changes to one process cannot be made in a vacuum; all processes must be coordinated and aligned so the entire system functions at an optimal level.

## SUMMARY

Change does not occur all at once. Redesign will not simply be implemented one Monday morning. During implementation, those involved will go through a "red zone," as shown in Figure 10.4.

The *red zone* is where the implementation of the new process has started and we are starting to end the old process—partly old way and partly new way. This is a critical period in which those doing the process are also going through a transition, which can be emotional and confusing. In a service organization, this period can have disastrous consequences. But careful monitoring, problem solving, and communications can minimize the risks involved.

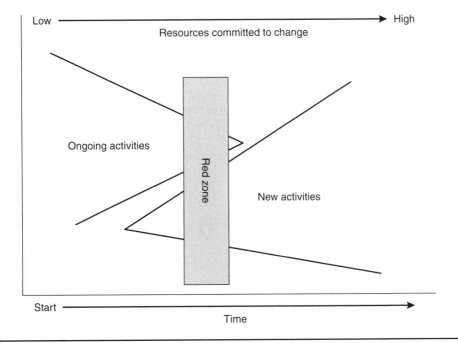

**Figure 10.4** Transitional time line.

Another potential problem midway through the changeover is the tendency to mix what is left of the old with the new, producing a hybrid that will not achieve an organization's objectives and may turn out to be worse than the old process. Staying attentive to the transition will ensure that everyone is kept informed, and as resources are freed up from the old system they can be redeployed to the new process in a planned, orderly manner.

The CPR process described in this chapter has a systematic, team-based methodology as its core for improving how work is accomplished effectively and efficiently in an organization. CPR is a structured process to deliver not only a redesigned process but organizational change as well.

Stated below are the "laws" we have learned from our involvement with the CPR process and redesign teams. We share them so that your redesign efforts will be successful.

## Laws of Core Process Redesign

1. All decisions must be driven by data. Confirm all assumptions.

2. Stay focused on meeting (or exceeding) customer requirements and fulfilling organizational strategy.

3. Fix whatever you can immediately.

4. Use ongoing measurement (both process and results) to keep yourself informed and on target.

5. The CPR phases are not completely linear—learn, recalibrate, and refocus as necessary.

6. Wallow in constructive conflict. Arbitrate with data.

7. Avoid "analysis paralysis" by testing best guesses.

8. Keep people who are not on the team informed.

9. Improvement work is continuous—you are never completely done—but do not forget to celebrate your successes.

# ENDNOTES

1. G. D. Beecroft, G. L. Duffy, and J. W. Moran, eds., *The Executive Guide to Improvement and Change* (Milwaukee, WI: ASQ Quality Press, 2003), Chapter 6 by R. A. Waks and J. W. Moran, pp. 67 – 80.
2. J. Bauer, G. Duffy, and R. T. Westcott, *The Quality Improvement Handbook,* 2nd ed. (Milwaukee, WI: ASQ Quality Press, 2006), 72.

3. R. Bialek, G. Duffy, and J. Moran, eds., *The Public Health Quality Improvement Handbook* (Milwaukee, WI: ASQ Quality Press, 2009).

4. Core Process Redesign (CPR) is a consulting and training product of RAW Consulting and is being used with permission as the basis of this chapter. Inquires regarding CPR should be sent to rawaks@aics.net or mastcove@myfairpoint.net.

5. M. Hammer and J. Champy, *Reengineering the Corporation: A Manifesto for Business Revolution* (London: HarperCollins, 1993).

6. Used with permission as the basis of this chapter. Inquiries regarding CPR should be sent to rawaks@aics.net or mastcove@myfairpoint.net.

# 11

# Developing the QFD Team

It takes a team of knowledgeable professionals to effectively perform a quality function deployment (QFD) study. Every team member involved in the project does not need to know everything about the process under study. Some team members will be special subject matter experts, involved in sharing detailed information about one piece of the activity. Other team members will be fully engaged throughout the entire project, from the chartering through identifying the critical to quality characteristics, and on through design, implementation, measurement, control, and documentation phases of the QFD.

The core members of the QFD team should have basic experience with the tools of quality improvement and the phases of a Lean-Six Sigma project. The more complex the QFD, the higher the level of skill in tools and team behaviors these core members should have in order to carry out the process improvement.

Successful organizations rely on the skills of a wide range of people to solve problems. This is where dynamic, productive teams make the difference. Teams create the environment in which members can keep up with change, learn more about the department, and develop collaborative skills.[1]

An effective team has the following characteristics:

- A group of two or more people working together to accomplish an objective.

- The team members are equally accountable for the accomplishment of a task and specific performance goals.

- Team members have complementary skills committed to a common purpose.

- A team combines the knowledge, experience, and skills of its members to achieve a synergistic effect.[2]

A team is appropriate when:

- Achieving an objective involves (or should involve) more than one organizational function. For example, to improve a health department grant writing process, the team may involve members from purchasing, project management, finance, client services, and key external agency partners.

- Some degree of isolation from the mainstream work is desirable for team members so they can focus on a specific objective or problem. For example, the strategic planning and quality manager for Orange County, FL, launched five year-long pilot projects to implement an integrated quality management system across the total health department. The projects were chosen to represent widely varied areas: septic system permitting, billing, training and education, database integrity, and expanded client services. The teams were strongly supported by champions in senior management level to ensure that sufficient time was allowed for the teams to fully develop and complete their projects. This support included funding of an external LSS Master Black Belt to train, mentor, and facilitate activities related to all five projects.

- Specially trained and experienced people are available when a specific need arises. Three examples are: (1) a "proposal response team" that is quickly assembled to address a request for proposal from a potential grant provider; (2) an audit review board that assembles when there is a feedback report to review and corrective action to resolve; and (3) a bilingual specialist in each clinic for special communication needs.

## TYPES OF TEAMS

Most health departments use teams to provide backup in crises, during heavy vacation periods, and in general activities when one person alone is not sufficient to meet a client or situational need. Six major types of teams organized for QI projects in Public Health departments are described:

*Natural Team*—A natural team (such as a work group or division) is made up of individuals who have responsibility for a specific process or function and who work together in a participative environment. Unlike the process improvement team, which is discussed next, the natural team is neither cross functional nor temporary. The team leader is generally the person responsible for the function or process performed within the work area. The natural team is useful in involving all employees in a work group engaged in continual improvement. Starting with one or two functions, successful natural teams can become role models for expansion of natural teams throughout an organization.

*Improvement Teams*—Process improvement teams, sometimes called PITs, focus on creating or improving a specific core process or support process. A PIT may attempt to completely reengineer a process or may work on incremental improvements (see Chapter 10). When undergoing a breakthrough improvement project, the team is usually cross functional in composition, with representatives from a number of functions possessing a range of skills related to the process to be improved. A PIT working on incremental improvements is often composed of persons having a functional interest in improving a portion of the overall process. Improvement teams implement most of the Public Health QI activities that are currently performed.

A specific type of process improvement used in LSS is the kaizen blitz or kaizen event. *Kaizen* is a Japanese word that means gradual continuous improvement. Kaizen teams are often formed to undertake an accelerated team approach in a time frame of three to five days. This approach can reduce cycle time and increase productivity by 70%.[3] Rapid cycle PDCA is a form of kaizen used by Public Health departments; applying the recurring sequence of PDCA for a brief period achieves improvement quickly.[4]

A quality improvement (QI) team has special features that differentiate it from a natural work team. A natural work team is usually within one department, often consists of the same discipline, involves ongoing functions of the organization, and is formal in that it appears on an organizational chart. A QI team, on the other hand, is typically cross departmental, interdisciplinary, created to serve a single purpose, and more informal.

*Cross-Functional Teams*—Cross-functional improvement teams focus on a major process within the whole health department as it impacts many functions. This is especially important if the objective of the PIT is to develop a breakthrough improvement (see Chapter 10).

In some cases, cross-functional teams carry out all or nearly all of the functions in a health department. In such cases, the department resembles a matrix- or project-type organization. In attempting to align functional groups, some organizations adopt cross-functional teams for many areas.

The smaller the department, the more likely it is that employees work together, often doing each other's designated jobs as the need arises. Most health departments are familiar with workforce constraints, which require each employee to wear many hats. In recent times, larger departments have come to recognize the value of smaller, cross-functional entities. These more flexible cross-functional teams can often reconfigure themselves more swiftly than larger divisions to meet changing needs.

*Project Teams*—A project team is formed to achieve a specific mission. The project team's objective may be to create something, such as a new immunization clinic or community prevention program. Typically, a project team employs full-time members, on loan from various units, for the duration of the project. The project team may or may not be cross functional in member composition, depending upon its objectives and competency needs. Often the project leader is the person to whom the ultimate responsibility for managing the resulting project outcome is assigned.

*Self-Directed Teams*—Self-directed (self-managed) teams are groups of employees authorized to make a wide range of decisions about how they will handle issues in a program. The responsibility can extend to safety, quality, scheduling of work, setting goals, work standards, equipment maintenance, and conflict resolution. Often called high-performance work teams, these teams offer employees a broader spectrum of responsibility and ownership of a process. Often the team members select the team leaders; sometimes leadership is rotated among members. Because of the level of empowerment afforded, careful planning and training are crucial to a successful self-directed team. The most success usually occurs when a new function or process is initiated. Transforming a traditional work culture to self-management is a lengthy process and is prone to potential workforce turmoil.

*Virtual Teams*—Virtual teams are groups of two or more individuals usually affiliated with a common function and a common purpose but who are not necessarily department employees. The nature of the virtual team is that its members conduct their work either partly or entirely via electronic communication. Virtual teams are a hybrid in that they may or may not be cross functional in terms of competencies. These teams may or may not be partly or entirely self-managed. Typically, the virtual team is geographically dispersed, in some cases with individual members working from home.

# THE VALUE OF TEAMS TO QFD

Different types of teams are used in an organization depending on the nature of a goal to be accomplished. The purpose of QFD is to find the critical requirements of the customer and to drill down into the workings of the department to meet those needs the best way, with the least amount of waste and the most effective use of people and resources.

A key principle is that no team should be formed unless its purpose and objectives can be traced upward in supporting the health department's strategies and plans. This alignment with organizational strategies, goals, and objectives should be shown through measurements directly related to the client or stakeholder requirements of the department.

Tools such as the balanced scorecard, voice of the customer, house of quality, customer or employee surveys, and focus groups are all effective vehicles for documenting the ultimate value of the team's work within the organization. Chapter 7, "Milestones and Measures: Interim and Final Reporting," describes characteristics and basic techniques for using measurements to facilitate QFD as a Lean-Six Sigma tool for Public Health. Teams contribute value during the steps of a QFD by using Lean-Six Sigma tools to gather and analyze data in order to make decisions that best meet customer needs.

Teams should be capable of demonstrating value. Every team, regardless of type, should address one or more of the following purposes:

- Fulfill a mandate (law, regulation, owners' requirements).

- Produce a favorable benefits-to-cost ratio for resources used.

- Provide a return on investment equal to or greater than an alternative project.

- Improve client satisfaction and retention.

- Meet or exceed client, stakeholder, or community expectations.

- Introduce new processes, programs, or services.

- Improve a process (cycle-time reduction, cost saving/avoidance, waste reduction).

- Increase a core competency.

- Build an effective and efficient workforce.

- Involve key stakeholders and partners in improvement initiatives.

- Enhance the health department reputation for delivering quality services.

Effective team performance is necessary for successfully designing and implementing QI projects in Public Health departments. QI projects always require teams to identify a process to improve, study the process, conduct tests of change, and implement a new process. Two distinguishing factors between teams that effectively conduct a QI project and teams that fail are the level of team skill and the effectiveness of team leadership. When QI projects fail, it is often because the team is ineffective.

The progression of steps within the QFD design model supports the effective development of teams. In the forming stage of team development, it is important for a QI team to have leadership support from all management levels in the health department. Many Public Health improvement projects go beyond the boundaries of the health department. Cross-functional teams can include members of other government agencies, community organizations, private companies, and other stakeholders. Appropriate individuals should be selected for the team. The house of quality (Figure 11.1) associates the voice of the customer with the technical requirements required within the health department to meet customer needs.

Five factors explain how teams are critical to success in quality improvement initiatives.[5] These factors should be considered in a Public Health department when a team enters the forming stage:

*Visualizing the Process Problem*—Quality problems are often not visible to individuals at senior management levels, but the problems can be experienced throughout an organization. The workers are often most aware of problems that have become systemic. The further a leader is removed from service delivery, the more difficult it is to see day-to-day problems. To identify quality problems, teams need individuals close to the problem who understand its impact.

*Front-line Staff*—Front-line Public Health staff are usually most knowledgeable about the process and its context. To understand a process, it is essential to have team participation by individuals who have the most detailed understanding of the process.

*Improvement Ideas*—Individuals at the front lines often have the most feasible suggestions for improvement. Not only does the front-line staff understand the process best, but they are also the most valuable source of improvement ideas.

*Support from All Levels*—Addressing quality problems requires the support of all individuals in the health department, not just those at senior level. Identifying and proposing solutions to quality problems is critical to QI efforts. Unless those involved in solution implementation fully understand the rationale for the effort, implementation is likely to fall short.

*Empowerment*—High-functioning teams empower people by providing opportunities for meaningful participation in problem identification and problem solving.

These five factors help a team in the forming stage because it ensures that individuals most familiar with the process are involved in the analysis and improvement of that process.

## PREPARING INDIVIDUALS TO BE EFFECTIVE TEAM MEMBERS

Teams are formed by organizing individuals around significant outcomes of value to the organization. Chartering an effective team and selecting the right people to be on the team is one of the major accomplishments of a successful leader. Basic observations useful in establishing an effective team include:

- The ultimate creators of quality products and services are people.

- People must be empowered from within to produce high-quality work.

- Quality is an attitude of mind.

- The cornerstone of personal quality is self-esteem, which empowers individuals to bring out the best in themselves.

- Organizational performance depends greatly on the personal quality of its members.

An effective leader builds the individual's self-esteem.

The organizational leader who charters a team has the responsibility to prepare individuals for successful teamwork. Individuals in the forming stage of a team require training for the challenges they will face during the process improvement journey. The team leader and sponsor are responsible for assessing the following for each of the team members:

- *Learning needs:* personal, identified, stated

- *Learning plan:* appropriate, achievable, real

- *Assessment plan:* assessments match the learning plan

The QFD matrix process includes the identification of personal learning needs based on the technical requirements for meeting customer needs. Once those technical requirements are validated in the QFD matrix, a learning plan is developed by the team leader using the criteria of "appropriate, achievable, and real." This learning plan includes documentation of training, records of performance, and verification of skill and tools application within the improvement project. Refer to Chapters 8 and 9 for more detail on LSS roles and responsibilities within teams.

## DEVELOP INDIVIDUALS INTO AN EFFECTIVE TEAM

The four stages of team development, beginning with the forming stage, may be effectively tracked in parallel with the progression of the four houses of quality, as seen in Figure 11.1. (More is available concerning the four stages of team development in an earlier text by the authors.[6]) As mentioned earlier, translating the voice of the customer into department requirements provides structure for focusing a team on desired customer outcomes.

Teams provide value at each phase of QFD, as reflected in the four houses of quality approach shown in Figure 11.1. During the VOC translation activities of House #1, the team may include clients, employees, technical specialists, internal leadership, and other stakeholders from the Macro, Meso, Micro, or Individual levels to identify overlapping requirements and impact. A critical goal of the first

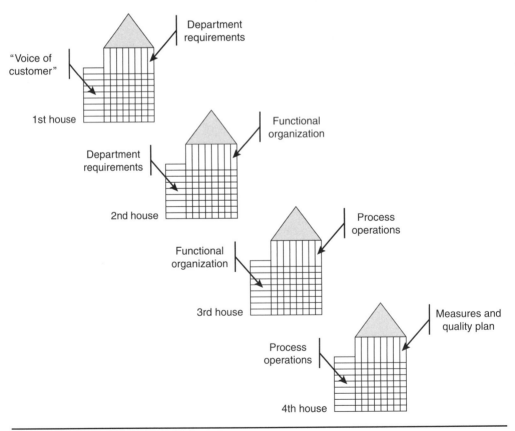

**Figure 11.1**　The four houses of quality.

house of quality is how to focus on improving the vital few things essential to goal achievement. These vital few things are known as critical to quality (CTQ).

Once the desired outcomes are understood clearly, the team moves its focus to the internal functions necessary to meet the customer requirements. House #2 in Figure 11.1 translates overall department requirements into objectives to be assigned to appropriate functions within the department. Team members need a cross-functional understanding of the department to translate external CTQ requirements to internal functional operations. Where house #1 activities identify the CTQ priorities, house #2 requires the team to assign these CTQs to functions within the health department.

Team members need good communication skills to involve others in the high-level design of solutions and removal of barriers to project success. The team must constantly monitor its progress to ensure that CTQ measures are being met by the actions proposed before going to house #3. QFD progressively translates the goals of the health department into the language of the people who perform the work. It is easy to get tied up in the details and lose sight of what the customer identified as priority outcomes. The storming characteristics of the second level of team formation may be visible during these conflicting dialogs. Validation back to the original requirements is a feedback loop for the team.

In house #3, the team defines the activities to improve the process. Strategy and tactics are set for the project in houses #1 and #2. Now the team identifies specific actions to continuously meet the identified customer requirements. What works for daily management? Chapter 1 introduced the value of QI tools in the daily management of a health department. Teams at the front lines write procedures, build flowcharts, identify valid measures, ensure sustainability of outputs, and establish training to encourage effective repetition of desired outcomes. Measures and monitoring align the goals in the department.[7] This understanding of how the process components all work together to meet customer needs leads team members into the norming stage of team development. Using the science of improvement in Public Health departments helps teams understand the processes and redesign them to work more efficiently. Major types of waste—rework, bottlenecks, waiting, redundancy, poor focus, and work unrelated to the health department's mission—can be identified and eliminated.

Finally, house #4 ties all the processes, measures, and outputs into a system that can be maintained, audited, and improved over the long term. This is truly the performing state of team development. The team creates a final report of the QFD project, which provides input into the department operations manual. Systems are established for monitoring and control, and training is created to ensure that the right people have the right skills to provide required products or services to end users. Front-line customer interfaces are put in place and tested to provide feedback on the new process. The cycle becomes continuous when this information is used to capture opportunities for future quality improvement.

The standardization of the processes established to meet the initial voice of the customer feeds directly back from house #4 to house #1 in a continuous loop of needs validation, process management, measurements, data analysis, and improvement. Teams involved in a QFD project are in a position to see the whole system of interconnected external customer needs and how internal functions are designed and implemented to meet those needs in a sustained manner.

Figure 11.2 is an example of how the voice of the customer flows into the voice of the process within the organization. The voice of the process reflects the technical requirements necessary for the organization to realize the outcomes desired by their clients. In Figure 11.2, the client/stakeholder influences both the health department's community relations side and the process owner and operations side. This "front office–back office" interrelationship is critical for a truly integrated system of customer satisfaction success. The transition from QFD house #1 with the voice of the customer quickly moves from the external needs gathering with the client into the technical translation of those needs into functional responsibilities within the health department units. The process owner assigns fulfillment tasks to front-line workers and specialists, who work with a program coordinator, who is closely in touch with program planners. These program planners are the feedback loop to the community relations arm of the organization, where validation and update of requirements back to the community

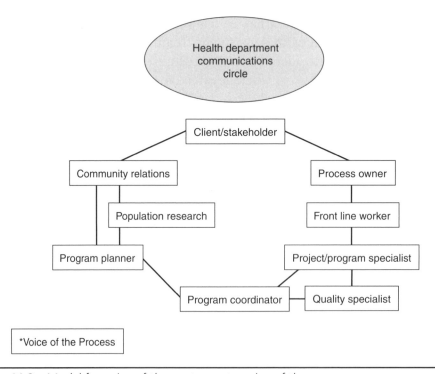

**Figure 11.2** Model for voice of the customer to voice of the process.

occur. This continuous loop is another form of the continuum of quality improvement described in Chapter 1.

A fifth stage of team formation is occasionally used: adjourning. The Lean-Six Sigma phase of control, including the measuring, monitoring, and documentation of improvements provides an excellent opportunity for the team to update policies, procedures, and operating documentation to hold the gains they have worked so hard to accomplish. Once the project close-out reviews have been completed, the team celebration culminates with adjournment. The skilled and experienced team members are now available for other, more challenging team assignments.

## TEAM DECISION MAKING

Decision making is one of the most exciting activities for a team. While much is written about continuous improvement and how to make it happen, less is known about the team decision-making process that goes along with improvement. Some of those decisions are not easy. This section considers several ways teams can support the long-term success of their organization through improved team decision making.

The trend toward employee involvement and cross-functional teams is spreading the decision-making opportunity to more members of the organization. Tom Pyzdek describes the transition of organizational structures from traditional hierarchical to modern cross-functional forms.[8] In organizations that use cross-functional structures, operational decisions as well as tactical and strategic decisions are moved away from top managers and more into the operating units. When employees are involved in team decision making, it is important to train them in decision-making skills.[9]

## THE DECISION-MAKING PROCESS

Decision-making is a process for analyzing pertinent data to make the optimum choice. Figure 11.3 suggests a progression in the effectiveness of improvement projects in which teams are engaged. Five stages of effectiveness are identified:

- *Initial:* Decisions are made based upon emotion or intuition rather than data

- *Managed:* Decisions are made using rudimentary tools to organize information

- *Defined:* Decisions are made using a defined approach to information gathering or problem solving

- *Quantitatively managed:* Decisions are made using structured data-gathering and analysis techniques

- *Optimizing:* Decision are made using data aligned to organizational processes and priority outcomes

The authors have worked with Public Health department process improvement teams at each of the five levels indicated. Public Health departments new to QI tend to mirror the initial characteristics of ad hoc, somewhat disorganized activity. Most Public Health professionals are highly motivated and learn quickly to move to higher levels of decision making.

Health department teams generally progress to the "managed" phase of team decision making during introductory training in the basic tools of quality improvement. Team decision skills advance to the "defined" level of performance when they are at the stage of writing a project charter, identifying sponsors and champions, defining outcomes, and achieving project milestones.

The transition to the "quantitatively managed" level of team decision making is significant. At this level, information supporting the problem statement is gathered in a structured and reliable manner. Data-based decision making is critical. Quantitative analysis of the current state of a process under study is required before the team can make recommendations to senior management. The Lean-Six Sigma tools are designed specifically to assist in gathering this quantitative data. Check sheets, surveys, control charts, histograms, probability functions, and value stream mapping all help the team identify numeric values for defects, client satisfaction, performance, waste, demand, and cycle time.

The last stage of team decision making, optimizing the performance, requires greater structure and planning. Lean-Six Sigma uses a quality function deploy-

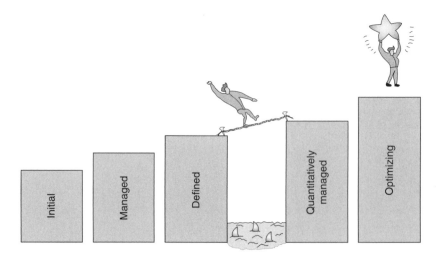

**Figure 11.3** Teams make decisions for continuous improvement.

ment method with a progression of matrices from initial mapping of voice of the customer to department requirements, then into detail of functional characteristics and process operations guides.

QFD and Lean-Six Sigma techniques support the gathering and analysis of data for decision making within the department. Although most problem solving requires decision making, not all decisions are made because there is a problem. Teams are not always charted to solve a problem. Incremental improvement and redesign (described in Chapter 10) are often employed to take advantage of new ideas or create different ways to meet community needs.

Whether for solving problems or simply to take advantage of a better idea, teams should employ the following decision-making steps:

1. Clearly state the decision purpose.

2. Establish the criteria (basis for decision and results required).

3. Assess criteria for those criterions that would be acceptable and measurable (identify the desirable criteria in order of priority).

4. Create a list of alternatives to consider, and collect data about each.

5. Assess the alternatives (relate each alternative solution back to the criteria and eliminate those that are unacceptable; weigh and prioritize remaining alternatives).

6. Conduct a risk analysis of the remaining alternatives (what could go wrong?).

7. Assess the risks (probability and seriousness of impact).

8. Make the decision (a decision with manageable and acceptable risk).[10]

## ATTRIBUTES OF A GOOD DECISION

The flow of a QFD project helps lead the team to good decisions. The team can evaluate the quality of a decision based on whether it:

- Represents the optimum in operational feasibility

- Involves a minimum of undesirable side effects and tradeoffs

- Is free from flaws that technical expertise could eliminate

- Delineates specific action commitments

- Is within the capacity of the affected people to comprehend and execute

- Is acceptable to those involved

- Is supportable with the resources that can be made available

- Includes provision for alignment, audit, and measurement

The use of decision matrices, prioritization exercises, and continuous validation of customer requirements in the process of drilling down through the QFD activities helps generate these attributes of a good decision.

## INFLUENCE AND CONTROL ISSUES FOR TEAM EFFECTIVENESS[11]

The more control the team has over a QI project, the less complex is the path to a successful project outcome. The level of control or influence authorized to the team surfaces early in the chartering of a new project. Figure 11.4 shows the level of control the team has on defining a discrete, measureable, and time-bound project aim statement decreasing as the issue under consideration moves farther from their immediate function. The less control the team has over events and decisions related to the project issue, the more the team must rely on influencing others to assist in reaching the desired future state.

During the charter discussion, the project sponsor and leader address the questions listed below and document the responses in the appropriate column of the table shown in Figure 11.5.

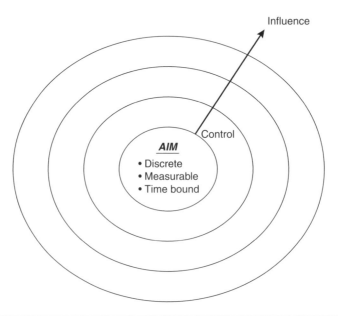

**Figure 11.4** Layers of team control and influence.

- Does the team have complete *control* over the element?

- Can the team *implement* a solution to this element when it is developed?

- To what extent must a team *involve and influence* others to get the element resolved?

- Is this element *outside the control and influence of the team*?

The answers to those four questions will help guide the team in developing a problem statement that will be workable for a project. Figure 11.5 uses an example of a mosquito-trapping program to illustrate the five activity elements (education, water, batteries, night trapping, motivation) and four components related to team control (control, implementation, influence, outside our influence). The first activity element, education, involves reducing inconsistency in the health department approach to mosquito trapping. This element is considered within the control of the QI team because it is empowered to implement education about mosquito trapping; equally important, the team sees the implementation of education to be within its purview. Likewise, the team does not need to involve or influence others to perform the education activity. Other activity elements listed in the lefthand column of the table have varying levels of external requirements for which the team must involve others.

Example: Reduce inconsistency mosquito trapping

| Element | Control | Implement | Involve and influence | Outside our control and influence |
|---------|---------|-----------|----------------------|-----------------------------------|
| Education | Within | Within | Within | In |
| Same water | Within | Within | Need influence | In |
| Batteries | Out | Within | Need influence | In |
| 1 night trapping | Within | Out | Need influence | In |
| Motivation | Out | Out | Need influence | Outside |

For each element, check which column(s) apply.
From this, select the area(s) of focus, develop a ranking of the elements to focus on, and write the problem statement for the quality improvement project to be started.

**Figure 11.5**   Components of the issue.

Choosing the elements that are totally within the control of the team may not be the best option, however. The issue statement components table provides a summary view of elements to be prioritized for overall impact to solve the issue. But education may not be the element that will make the most difference to the future state. If "same water" is identified as a stronger root cause of inconsistencies in mosquito trapping, the team has identified in the fourth column that they will need to secure assistance from parties who have stronger control or influence. The fifth column assessment of the "same water" element indicates that this influence is likely to be secured, should the team choose to pursue it.[12]

## The Problem Statement as a Vehicle for Norming

An issue involving a single operational unit is generally easier to control than one that has cross-functional impact or that involves many groups. The more internal the issue, the more discrete the problem statement tends to be, as shown in Figure 11.6. In addition the more discrete problem statements are operational rather than strategic as shown in Figure 11.7. An example of such a statement is:

*How do we identify who has immediate needs, such as immunization services, in the community our health department is chartered to address, identify those needs, and develop a program to respond to those needs within the next 30 days?*

The focus of the statement is internal to the health department and within their control or influence to address. If the problem statement encompassed long-

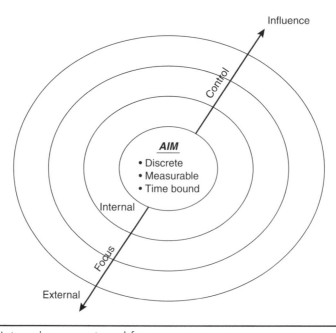

**Figure 11.6**   Internal versus external focus.

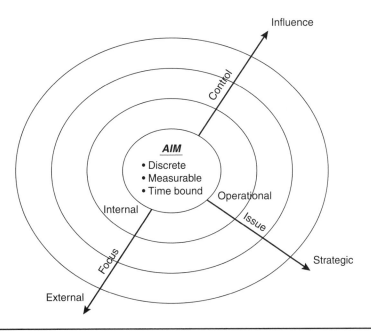

**Figure 11.7** Operational versus strategic issue.

term trends for broad community services beyond the mandate of the health department, the focus would be more strategic, involving external partners such as other municipal agencies and extending the time line well beyond the concise, 30-day deadline.

Figure 11.7 adds the planning impact dimension (from operational to strategic) related to the issue under consideration. An internal issue totally under the control of a single business unit is generally more short term or operational. As an issue encompasses more cross-functional processes, outside suppliers or community partners, the scope tends toward a longer-term resolution or a strategic approach for problem solving.

## DEVELOP MEASURES TO MAINTAIN
## PROCESS IMPROVEMENT

During the project charting process, the team develops high-level measures for the elements of the problem statement that will help the team know (and share with others) that the changes proposed and implemented have had a positive impact. The most common measures are process, capacity, and outcome, as shown in Figure 11.8. Process measures are the most operational. They are taken as work is performed. Capacity measures have a longer window for gathering data. The performance of several processes may be required to assess the capacity of a program to provide services to the community. Finally, outcome measures are the

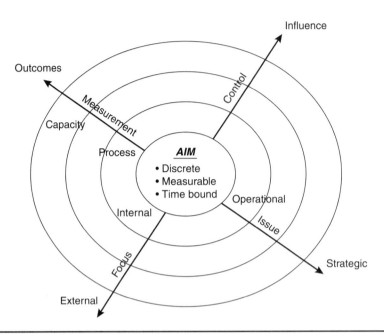

**Figure 11.8**   Process, capacity, outcomes measurement.

most strategic. Figure 11.8 provides examples of common measures in a Public Health department for each of the three categories.

In the example of mosquito trapping in Figure 11.5, the process of educating the public on the need for mosquito trapping may take one hour to perform. The capacity of the health department to set traps for the mosquitoes may involve a number of processes over a period of time. Achieving the outcome of reducing the inconsistency of mosquito trapping with the final goal of controlling the mosquito population may take months and the involvement of multiple departments within the county.

When developing measures, the team should select measures that are easy to collect and calculate. The measures are then aligned with the change wanted at all levels. Done in this manner, the measures promote accountability by the team. Examples of some currently used measures at health departments are shown in Figure 11.9. Each of these measures can be tied directly to a function within the health department. They are discrete and measurable and can be bound by an appropriate time frame for the scope of the issue the team is addressing.[13]

## SET THE TIME FRAME FOR IMPLEMENTATION

An implementation time frame for achieving the improved results is estimated by the QI team. The implementation time line starts in broad terms and becomes more specific as the team identifies alternative solutions and implements the best op-

| Measurement examples for short term and long term performance targets | | |
|---|---|---|
| Process | Capacity | Outcome |
| • No-show WIC appointments | • Health department workforce turnover | • Influenza deaths |
| • Percent of women who receive adequate prenatal care | • Completion of annual health profile by every LHD | • Multi-drug resistant tuberculosis cases |
| • Education on consistent mosquito trapping techniques | • Lobby wait times for client services | • Reduced obesity in target population |
| | | • Improved water quality in county reservoirs |

**Figure 11.9**  Measurement examples for performance.

tion. Initially the team may establish a time line with an end date for the project, a schedule for team meetings, team training, and meetings with the team sponsor. Once the problem solving is complete and the solution approved, the team can revise the time line to include more specific implementation tasks. Figure 11.10 is a Gantt chart developed by the Saginaw County Department of Public Health for an improvement project undertaken in 2008.[14] The Gantt chart is a specific type of time line and is very useful for QI team project management. The Gantt chart is a bar chart that shows the tasks of a project, when each must take place, and how long each will take. As the project progresses, bars are shaded to show tasks that have been completed. People assigned to each task also can be shown.

## Establish a Communication Plan

The team sponsor and champion are responsible for identifying the people who will be involved in or affected by the project. These persons may be participants, subject matter resources, advisors, or customers of the future-state process. The team must consider what these stakeholders' concerns may be about the activities or results of the project. Team members make preliminary decisions about how to keep these individuals and groups informed throughout the project. Actions should be included within the project to address stakeholder concerns and resolve these issues to the satisfaction of the individuals impacted. The communication plan includes standard updates as well as special information on issues that may arise and affect short- or long-term outcomes related to the project.

When people are involved in decisions affecting them, they are more likely to support change because they feel more in control and are more likely to understand the reasons for the change. A communication plan is often part of the overall project plan.[15] Figure 11.11 is an example of the communication plan included in the project charter for the Saginaw County Public Health Department in a 2008 accreditation preparation project.[16] The communication plan shows who the target

Saginaw County Department of Public Health Gantt chart

NACCHO accreditation pilot grant 2008

| Task: Saginaw County HD | 29 Feb | 7 Mar | 14 Mar | 21 Mar | 28 Mar | 1 Apr | 10 Apr | 15 Apr | 21 Apr | 1 May | 8 May | 13 May | 19 May | 27 May | 28 May | 6 Jun | 13 Jun |
|---|---|---|---|---|---|---|---|---|---|---|---|---|---|---|---|---|---|
| Finalize self assessment analysis | X | | | | | | | | | | | | | | | | |
| Align with SCPHD mod squad | X | | | | | | | | | | | | | | | | |
| Identify priority project | X | | | | | | | | | | | | | | | | |
| Plan PHF consultant visit | | X | | | | | | | | | | | | | | | |
| Set agenda and travel schedule | | X | | | | | | | | | | | | | | | |
| Saginaw/PHF PI meeting | | | X | | | | | | | | | | | | | | |
| Plan pilot PI project and milestones | | | X | X | | | | | | | | | | | | | |
| Validate PHF hours remaining | | | X | | X | X | X | X | X | X | X | X | X | | X | | |
| Teleconference consultant update | | | | | | | X | X | X | | X | X | X | | | | |
| Decide team meeting schedule | | | | | X | 1:30 | 2:30 | 1:30 | 10:00 | 10:30 | 10:00 | 10:00 | 9:00 | 9:00 | 10:00 | | |
| Hold formal team meetings | | | | | X | X | X | X | X | TRG. | X | X | | | | | |
| Complete team charter | | | | | X | | | | | | | | | | | | |
| Flowchart desired staff trg proc | | | | | | | X | | | | | | | | | | |
| Analyze causes of staff exp issues | | | X | | | | | | | | | | | | | | |
| Select solutions as appropriate | | | X | | | | | | | | | | | | | | |
| Design training | | | X | X | X | X | X | X | X | | | | | | | | |
| Establish measures and outcomes | | | | | | | | | | | | X | X | | | | |
| Conduct training | | | | | | | | | | X | | | | | | | |
| Gather measures and analyze | | | | | | | | | | X | X | | | | | | |
| Analyze and modify process as needed | | | | | | | | | | | X | X | X | X | X | X | X |
| Monitor competency levels (6 wk eval) | | | | | | | | | | X | X | | | | | | |
| Measure pilot | | | | | | | | | | X | | | | | | | |
| Create report of improved outcomes | | | | | | | | | | | | X | X | X | X | | |
| Final report and storyboard | | | | | | | | | | | | | | X | X | X | X |
| Final NACCHO/PHF report by 5/31/08 | | | | | | | | | | | | | | | X | X | X |

**Figure 11.10**   Gantt chart for implementation time line.

| Who | Main concerns | Communication notes (when and how you will communicate with them) |
| --- | --- | --- |
| E-team and staff | An introduction to CQI processes | Received training |
| Ditto | Quality terminology is unfamiliar | Received training |
| Governing entities (BOC, BOH, advisory boards) | Involvement and updates | Receive the report after 5/31/08 |
| Mod squad | The strategic planning process | Update monthly |
| NACCHO and the PHF | Receive updates | Via the health officers report |
| The community | Community health assessment | Is completed after May 2008 |

**Figure 11.11** Sample communication plan.

of planned communication efforts are, what the main concerns of those targeted individuals might be, and what information should be communicated to them.

# SUMMARY

Teams make critical contributions to department success at each level of the Macro–Meso–Micro–Individual continuous quality improvement system in Public Health. Continuous improvement opportunities exist in each of the four levels. When working at the Macro level, the health department should involve a variety of internal and external participants to ensure that accurate information is available upon which to make effective decisions. Senior leadership often creates partnerships with key clients and sponsors to better anticipate direction in the community. By listening to clients, suppliers, shareholders, funders, and employees, department officers can better understand the priorities and direction for continued success.

At the Meso level, managers translate decisions made at the Macro level into functional requirements for the department. This is where QFD is employed. Here it is important to actively involve employees from many levels of the health department in decisions to better understand the impact of changes in processes and policies. The daily management activities of the Micro level use the sequenced steps of QFD to break long-term opportunities into specific, internal operations that can be assigned to personnel and measured for effectiveness.

Operational decisions deal more with the day-to-day issues of running a program. At the Individual level, employee input is critical in making decisions. The benefits of employee empowerment and involvement in operational decision making have been described in this chapter. Modern management training supports the use of departmental and cross-functional teams to assess current situations and make recommendations for improvement. When team decision making is successfully implemented, the role of management becomes more that of resource provider and expediter, rather than initial decision maker. Using teams to orchestrate a QFD project gives two important benefits: The QFD structure guides decision making from external need to detailed internal processes, and the innovation of skilled team members ensures that the best ideas are presented for a maximum solution.

# ENDNOTES

1. P. R. Scholtes, B. L. Joiner, and B. J. Streibel, *The TEAM Handbook,* 3rd ed. (Madison, WI: Oriel, 2003), p. 1-1.
2. J. E. Bauer, G. L. Duffy, and R. T. Westcott, eds., *The Quality Improvement Handbook,* 2nd ed. (Milwaukee, WI: ASQ Quality Press, 2006).
3. M. L. George, *Lean Six Sigma for Service* (New York: McGraw Hill, 2003), pp. 337–341.
4. G. Duffy, J. Moran, and W. Riley, *Rapid Cycle PDCA* (The Quality Texas Foundation Update Bi-monthly newsletter, August 2009). www.texas-quality.org.
5. B. Fried and W. R. Carpenter, "Understanding and Improving Team Effectiveness in Quality Improvement," in C. P. McLaughlin and A. D. Kaluzny, eds., *Continuous Quality Improvement in Healthcare,* 3rd ed. (Sudbury, MA: Jones and Bartlett, 2006).
6. R. Bialek, G. Duffy, and J. Moran, eds., *The Public Health Quality Improvement Handbook* (Milwaukee, WI: Quality Press, 2009), Chapter 22, W. Riley and H. Parsons, "The Reality of Teams in Resource-Constrained Public Health."
7. More on daily management is available in Chapter 1 in R. Bialek, G. Duffy, and J. Moran, eds., *The Public Health Quality Improvement Handbook* (Milwaukee, WI: Quality Press, 2009).
8. T. Pyzdek, "Organizational Structure for Quality," in *The Essence of Quality Management,* no. 1 (Milwaukee, WI: ASQ Quality Management Division, 1997).
9. G. D. Beecroft, G. L. Duffy, and J. W. Moran, eds., *The Executive Guide to Improvement and Change* (Milwaukee, WI: ASQ Quality Press, 2002).
10. Bauer, Duffy, and Westcott, *The Quality Improvement Handbook.*
11. L. Beitsch, G. Duffy and J. Moran, "Ready, AIM, Problem Solve," *Texas Quality Foundation Newsletter* (October 2009).
12. Used with permission: Reduce Inconsistency Mosquito Trapping QI Project, Tulsa City-County Health Department, (September 2008).
13. G. Duffy, Presentation to the Florida Public Health Association, (Palm Beach Gardens, FL, August 6, 2009).
14. R. Bialek, G. Duffy, and J. Moran, Editors, *The Public Health Quality Improvement Handbook*, (ASQ Quality Press, 2009), Chapter 8. Saginaw County Public Health Department QI team, (2009).
15. P. R. Scholtes, B. L. Joiner, and B. J. Streibel, The Team Handbook, 3rd ed. (Oriel Incorporated, Waunakee, WI, 2003): 1–12.
16. R. Bialek, G. Duffy, and J. Moran, Editors, *The Public Health Quality Improvement Handbook*, (ASQ Quality Press, 2009), Chapter 8. Saginaw County Department of Public Health QI team, (2009).

# 12

# Conducting a QFD Study

In Chapter 1 the QFD process was described as a series of matrices for program or service design or redesign. In this chapter we will review four matrices necessary for a system-level design or redesign of a program or service.

Matrices are identified by a letter and a number to describe their position in the matrix of matrices. The matrices are a series of L-shaped matrixes, as shown in Figure 12.1, that show relationships among two groups of information, such as A to B or comparing one set of information to itself such as A to A. These matrices help identify the connecting points between items and prioritize these items to facilitate decision making. When a roof is added to a matrix, it takes the form shown in Figure 12.6 known as a "house of quality."

The matrix nomenclature is shown in Figure 12.2. The matrix nomenclature describes an item's location in the matrix by a row location designated as "i" and a column location designated by "j." Both the row and column location are usually assigned a numerical location such as a11, this is where row 1 intersects column 1. The matrix does not have to have an equal number of rows and columns.

These QFD matrices are used to translate customer wants and needs into the most important functional features needed to satisfy these stated needs and wants.

Chapter 11 addressed how to charter, form, train, and monitor the QFD team. The chartering and formation of the QFD team is a process that is critical to the overall success of the effort. The charter clearly defines what the QFD team will be analyzing in order to make recommendations on how to achieve the ultimate goal of satisfying the customer. The right people need to be selected for the team, and these are usually the ones who can make decisions. Each step in the QFD process needs to have decisions made, and for that reason the QFD team needs to be composed of decision makers from various disciplines. This chapter focuses on the mechanics of using QFD.

Chapter 4 discussed the importance of capturing the voice of the customer, both internal and external, as the first step in using a QFD process. We must

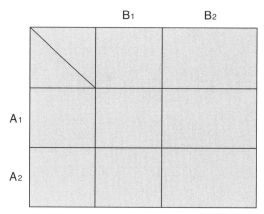

Source: http://www.asq.org/learn-about-quality/new-management-planning-tools/overview/matrix-diagram.html.

**Figure 12.1** L-shaped matrix.

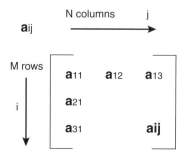

**Figure 12.2** M × N matrix.

understand and interpret what the customer expects and needs from each function. The VOC is composed of a mixture of items that describe the wants, needs, quality characteristics, functions, elements, process characteristics, and reliability that are expected from the organization. It is important to sort out the customer's voice into categories that compose inputs into other matrices that will be used. The wants and needs are ranked by importance to the customer using a scale of 1 (low importance), 3 (medium importance), and 5 (high importance). The VOC drives the QFD process, and it is important to understand the importance of each item to the customer. Each item is weighted to construct measures of the attribute to develop a matrix. The time invested in obtaining an accurate VOC is well worth the effort since it is the input to the house of quality.

This weighting of the various attributes as we move through the matrices will help to sort the data to focus us on the key functions that are most likely to satisfy the customer.

Key items can be analyzed further into components using a tree diagram as shown in Figure 12.3. This allows the team to explore a key element based on its sub-elements if further understanding is necessary.

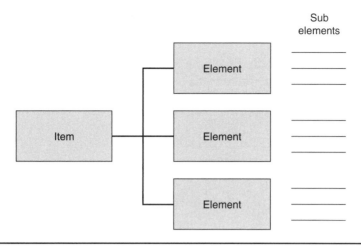

**Figure 12.3**   Tree diagram.

Five concepts used in the QFD model are:

- *Quality characteristics:* Critical characteristics that are measurable items that ensure that the customer's needs and wants will be met

- *Function:* Tasks necessary for the product or service to be deliverable and acceptable to the customer

- *Concept:* Method for achieving functions

- *Element:* Item needed for achieving the best concept

- *Relationships:* How items relate to one another, and the relationship is defined as a 1 (weak relationship), 3 (medium relationship), or 9 (strong relationship)

An overview of the QFD system level analysis is shown in Figure 12.4. The four steps representing the house of quality are shown in Figure 12.4, a model to (1) determine customer requirements, (2) translate the requirements to functions (tasks) to accomplish them, (3) create the process to produce the outcomes, (4) implement the process, and (5) monitor process variation. These steps show how QFD compliments the PDC/SA cycle with some tools and techniques to help in each phase of the cycle. The QFD sequence of steps translates customer requirements to functions to accomplish them, to process characteristics, to how to implement and monitor the function, to ensure that the targets set are being achieved.

Figure 12.5 expands Figure 12.4 into the various houses of quality that are used to progress from a system-level program, product, or service design or redesign.

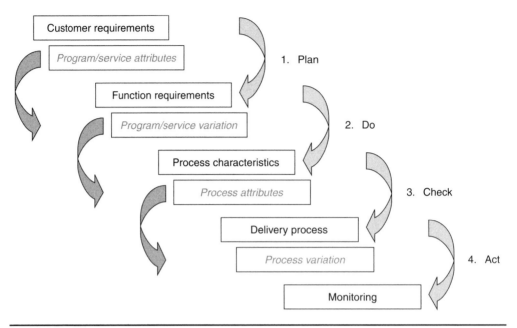

**Figure 12.4** The system-level QFD approach.

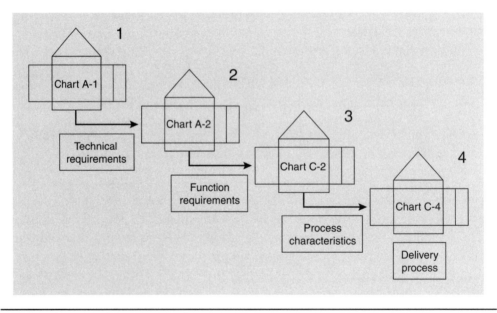

**Figure 12.5** Four houses of quality.

A QFD study usually starts with chart A-1, which is the original house of quality shown in Figure 12.6 because this is the chart that uses the VOC that we have prioritized.

The left side of chart A-1 contains the customer demands with their weighting of importance. The weighting can be accomplished during the capturing of the VOC or later using focus groups. The customer demands are sometimes re-ferred to as the "whats."

Once the customer demands have been assessed, the QFD team develops the critical characteristics that will achieve these customer demands. These critical characteristics, sometimes referred to as the voice of the organization (VOO), are placed on the top of Chart A-1 and will be compared to the customer demands. Another designation for the critical characteristics is "hows."

The QFD team develops the critical characteristics, which are measurable items that will address the customer demands. This development of the critical characteristics is accomplished through a brainstorming session, and then these ideas are grouped into categories using an affinity diagram. The elements within these major groupings are what we place on the top of chart A-1.

One thing we want to ensure as we post the customer demands and critical characteristics on chart A-1 is that they are of the same level of thinking. Usually if we can ensure that these items are at the second level of the tree diagram it will make the comparisons easier. This keeps the comparisons at the same level and ensures that a high-level item does not overwhelm the rest of the items. If you find when filling out chart A-1 that one item correlates to all the items, it is probably at a higher level than it should be and needs to be broken down into its next level of components.

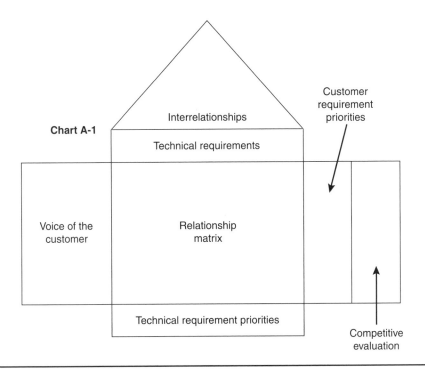

**Figure 12.6** House of quality.

The next step is to analyze the customer demands and critical characteristics in a pair-wise comparison process to develop the relationships and their strengths between them.

The right side of the matrix is where the customer's perception of the service is analyzed. These perceptions can be assessed using accreditation standards or national benchmarks. This analysis will help understand the extent to which the program satisfies the customer and how much improvement is needed. Once this is completed, the next step is to (1) develop a weighting of the critical characteristics and (2) establish their target values.

Once the characteristics have been identified, they are placed on the top of chart A-1. The next step is to develop the functions to achieve the critical characteristics. The key functions are then transferred to the left side of chart A-2, and the QFD team then develops the elements that need to be placed along the top of the relationship matrix in A-2 which define the process characteristics needed to achieve customer requirements as identified in chart A-1.

Once the key process characteristics are known, the system-level overview can be completed by specifying how to design the program or service. Finally, the delivery plan will ensure that those needing or requiring the program or service understand how to obtain it. Some of the delivery items may involve aspects of communication and marketing.

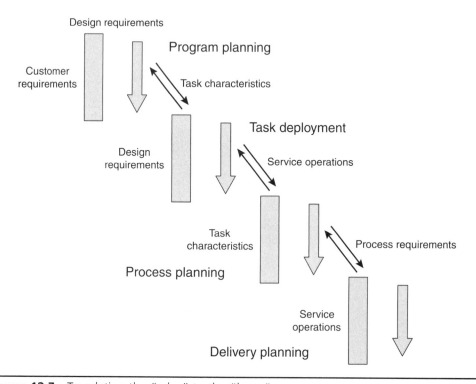

**Figure 12.7**   Translating the "who" to the "how."

At this point we now have a system level design of a program or service. The details of the plan will be developed as the process is implemented by the specific units throughout the organization that will be involved in accomplishing the defined targets for the customer requirements.

Figure 12.7 gives some hints on which other charts may be helpful in completing a subsystem design. At the subsystem level, many combinations of charts can be used, and it is not possible to give a precise road map because the project's scope will determine which charts are needed.

Appendix B lists software that can assist you in using QFD and calculating the values within the matrices. The authors do not endorse any particular software but encourage the reader to evaluate all that are listed and others that may surface to find what fits their particular needs.

# 13

# Navigating the QFD Matrices

This chapter is an introduction to the mechanics of constructing a QFD chart. The purpose of QFD charts is to develop weights for the characteristics being compared to prioritize the most important ones and concentrate scarce resources. The matrices are interconnected in that weights set for a characteristic transfer from one matrix to the next.

The development of the weights is an important task for the design or development team because it requires them to reach consensus for each paired comparison they make in a matrix. In order to make these paired comparisons, the design or development team must build a collective in-depth knowledge of their product or service, understand how the customer will use the product or service, and how the customer (internal and external) prioritizes their demands.

In Chapter 4 we developed the way to capture the voice of the internal and external customer and detailed the importance of why it should be done and the care that must taken to get a clear, accurate voice of the customer. To further emphasize the importance of a clear and accurate voice of the customer, we use VOC in the first matrix to develop the "demanded weight." This demanded weight is used to develop the other weights that are transfered to the next matrix. Because the VOC is the initial input, which carries throughout the remaining matrices, it is extremely important that it is accurate. If it is flawed, it will contaminate the rest of the process and produce questionable results.

The first chart most design teams use is known as chart A-1 (see Appendix A) or the house of quality because of its shape (see Figure 13.1). Chart A-1 is composed of six components (labeled A–F). Each part will be discussed separately so the reader understands how each component functions separately and as part of the whole matrix. Chart A-1 is a complex matrix that contains information prioritized into the most important pieces for design focus. Chart A-1 is a matrix the design and development team should revisit regularly. It must be up to date and any changes to the weights will impact the rest of the matrices that are developed.

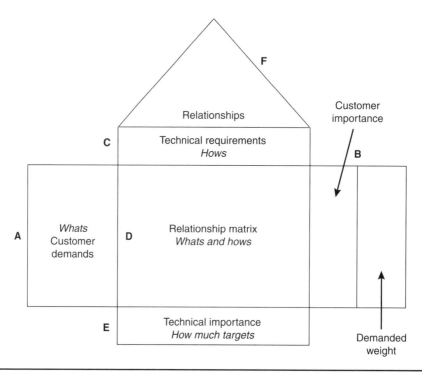

**Figure 13.1**  Chart A-1: The house of quality.

*Component A*—Developing the customer demands—"The whats"

In Chapter 4, developing the customer demands for a product or service was discussed. The customer demands are captured through a variety of surveying methods and then synthesized in a voice of the customer table (Figure 4.6). The output of the VOC table is the development of a VOC tree diagram as shown in Figure 13.2. This tree diagram is developed by arranging the VOC table items into the same level of detail. Usually we go out to two or three levels to get the VOC in the same level of detail. To explain how all the components of chart A-1 work, the level of detail has been taken to two levels and is generalized for any Public Health service for illustration purpose. Each one of the VOC items are then rated on a scale of 1 (low) to 5 (high) importance to the customer using the data from customer surveys. If we do take the VOC inputs down to the same level of detail, we run the risk of everything correlating to everything—they are too global in scope and need to be broken down into more discrete items. This is true for any of the inputs we develop for consideration in any of the matrices—the more discrete the level of detail the better.

*Component B*—This left side of side of the A-1 matrix is composed of seven parts—columns 2 through 8 as shown in Table 13.1. Column

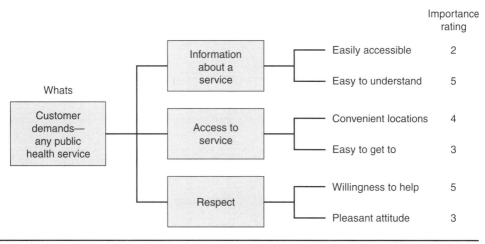

Importance rating

**Figure 13.2** VOC tree diagram.

1 is a transfer of the customer demands from the VOC tree diagram in Figure 13.2.

Column 1: Customer demands—These are listed from the VOC tree diagram and are the second or third level of detail.

Column 2: Importance rating— The customer demands in column 1 are rated on a scale of 1 (low) to 5 (high) importance to the customer using the data from customer surveys, interviews, or focus groups.

Column 3: Current performance—The customer demands are rated on the same scale as column 2, but now the rating is how we are currently performing in meeting that demand.

Column 4: Improvement target—Now we establish a realistic improvement target for each of the customer demands that could be accomplished in some time period, usually six months to one year. The design or development team must decide what amount of improvement they can realistically accomplish given time and resource constraints

Column 5: Improvement ratio—Divide the current performance into the improvement target.

Column 6: Touch point/sales point—Each customer demand is analyzed to determine whether it is a sales point (would entice the customer to use our product) or touch point (where the customer touches the process) and is rated on a scale of 1 (not a sales or touch point), 1.2 (sales or touch point), or 1.5 (a very strong sales or touch point). These

**Table 13.1** A-1 Matrix for weighted customer importance.

| 1 | 2 | 3 | 4 | 5 | 6 | 7 | 8 |
|---|---|---|---|---|---|---|---|
| **Whats customer demands** | **Importance rating** | **Current performance** | **Improvement target** | **Improvement ratio** | **Touch point/ sales point** | **Demanded weight** | **Absolute weight** |
| Easily accessible | 2 | 2 | 3 | 1.5 | 1.2 | 3.6 | 10.6 |
| Easy to understand | 5 | 3 | 4 | 1.1 | 1.5 | 8.3 | 24.3 |
| Convenient locations | 4 | 2 | 2 | 1 | 1.0 | 4.0 | 11.7 |
| Easy to get to | 3 | 1 | 1 | 1 | 1.2 | 3.6 | 10.6 |
| Willingness to help | 5 | 4 | 5 | 1.3 | 1.2 | 7.8 | 22.9 |
| Pleasant attitude | 3 | 2 | 3 | 1.5 | 1.5 | 6.8 | 19.9 |
| Σ | | | | | | 34.1 | 100% |

sales or touch points are places that, if we make improvements and meet the customer importance level, will improve the customer's satisfaction with our product or service each time it is used.

Column 7: Demanded weight—This is calculated by multiplying column 2 by column 5 by column 6. These weights are then summed.

Column 8: Absolute weight—Each demanded weight is converted to a percentage of the total. This is the weight we will use in our calculations of the hows.

Once we have developed the weight for the customer demands, it is time to develop the means or the hows. How we will meet the customer demands. Other names for the hows are technical characteristics and substitute quality characteristics.

> *Component C*—Developing the hows—Technical characteristics or substitute quality characteristics are measureable items that will help accomplish the whats. The hows are developed by the product or service design team, which looks at each customer demand and develops ways to meet that demand. The use of a solution and effect diagram,[1] as shown in Figure 13.3, is a method to develop the hows. For each customer demand, the design and development team can brainstorm and organize their ideas on the

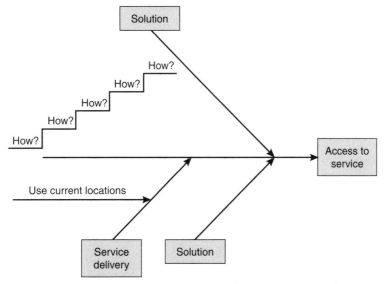

Source: *The Public Health Quality Improvement Handbook*, R. Bialek, G. Duffy, J. Moran, Editors, Quality Press, © 2009, pp. 185–187.

**Figure 13.3**   Solution and effect diagram.

solution and effect diagram and then prioritize them into the most likely candidates to satisfy the customer demands. The hows must be measurable items that ensure that the customer demands are satisfied.

Once all the prioritized hows are developed, they can be sorted using an affinity diagramming process into like categories. These categories can be arranged in a tree diagram like the design and development team did for the customer demands as shown in Figure 13.4. Once we have the hows at the second level of detail in the tree diagram, they will form the top of the matrix in component C. This is shown in Table 13.2.

> *Component D*—Table 13.2 is component D of the house of quality and the top of Table 13.2 is component C. In this part of the house of quality we develop the relationships between the whats and the hows. We compare each how to each what using a paired comparison process and rate the strength of the relationships as either strong (9), medium (3), weak (1), or no relationship (blank). It should be noted that for illustrative purposes there are an equal number of whats and hows but in a real QFD study there may be different numbers of whats and hows—it does not have to be equal.

Once all the relationships have been agreed, to the weight for the hows is established. The weight for the hows are obtained by multiplying the relationship strength by the absolute weight from component B. The sums are totaled down the columns and then a total weight is calculated as in component B, which is then converted to a percentage weight of the total, as shown in Table 13.2.

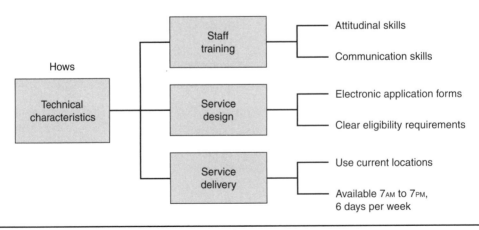

**Figure 13.4**  Technical characteristics tree diagram.

**Table 13.2** Component D: House of quality weighting of whats and hows.

| Whats/Hows | Attitudinal skills | Communication skills | Electronic application form | Clear eligibility requirements | Use current locations | Available 7AM-7PM/6 days/week | Absolute weight column |
|---|---|---|---|---|---|---|---|
| Easily accessible | | | | | 3 | 9 | 10.6 |
| Easy to understand | | 3 | 9 | 9 | | | 24.3 |
| Convenient locations | | | | | 3 | | 11.7 |
| Easy to get to | | | | | 9 | | 10.6 |
| Willingness to help | 9 | 9 | | 3 | | | 22.9 |
| Pleasant attitude | 9 | 9 | | | | | 19.9 |
| Total weight | 385.2 | 458.1 | 218.7 | 287.4 | 162.3 | 94.5 | 1606.2 |
| Absolute % weight | 24.0 | 28.5 | 13.6 | 17.9 | 10.1 | 5.9 | 100% |

*Component E*—In this part of the A-1 matrix we develop the how muches of the hows, as shown in Table 13.3, which is an expansion of Table 13.2. In this component we want to develop the following:

- Target value: This is what we want to aim for in developing our product or service. The electronic forms have a target of 3 forms.

- **Direction:** The direction is shown as (↑) "up" meaning we would want more, (↓) "down" meaning we would want less, or blank meaning the current value is sufficient. For our electronic forms we see that the arrow is down, meaning fewer forms is best.

- **Unit:** This is the measurement unit that we can track the hows against.

The completion of Table 13.3 is the final piece of the house of quality, and can be quite large. The authors recommend using software to develop the table and calculate the various weights because its size can make it impossible to do by hand. Appendix B lists some commonly used software packages which the reader can investigate to determine which is most appropriate for their needs.

The important hows would now be transferred to chart 2, as shown in Figure 13.5, to develop the functions that would support the hows. These functions would be weighted in a similar fashion as done for the hows because the weights for the hows in chart 1 would be transferred to chart 2.

The important functions would then be transferred to chart 3 to develop the process characteristics to make the functions a reality. The important process

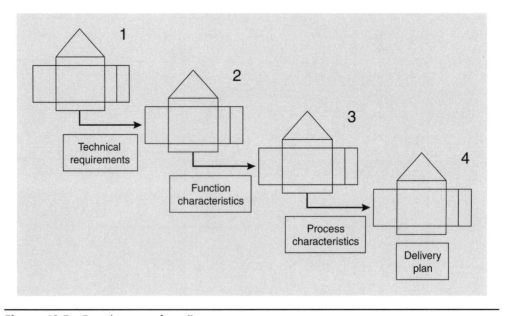

**Figure 13.5** Four houses of quality.

**Table 13.3**   Matrix to calculate measurement targets for product or service outcomes.

| Whats/Hows | Attitudinal skills | Communication skills | Electronic application form | Clear eligibility requirements | Use current locations | Available 7AM-7PM/6 days/week | Absolute weight column |
|---|---|---|---|---|---|---|---|
| Easily accessible | | | | | 3 | 9 | 10.6 |
| Easy to understand | | 3 | 9 | 9 | | | 24.3 |
| Convenient locations | | | | | 3 | | 11.7 |
| Easy to get to | | | | | 9 | | 10.6 |
| Willingness to help | 9 | 9 | | 3 | | | 22.9 |
| Pleasant attitude | 9 | 9 | | | | | 19.9 |
| Total weight | 385.2 | 458.1 | 218.7 | 287.4 | 162.3 | 94.5 | 1606.2 |
| Absolute % Weight | 24.0 | 28.5 | 13.6 | 17.9 | 10.1 | 5.9 | 100% |
| **Component E** | | | | | | | |
| Target value | | | 3 | 10 | 15 | 12 | |
| Direction | ← | ← | → | → | ← | ← | |
| Unit | | | # Forms | # Requirements | # Locations | # Hours | |

characteristics would be transferred to chart 4 to develop the ways in which the product or service would be delivered.

The purpose of this chapter is to introduce the reader to the basics of QFD matrices. Many books go into more details of QFD. A list of recommended references is provided in Appendix C.

It is strongly recommended that when first using QFD you engage an experienced facilitator to guide the design or development team through the matrices, the process, the interpretation of the output of the matrices, and which matrices to use to get the best design.

## ENDNOTES

1. Source: R. Bialek, G. Duffy, and J. Moran, eds., *The Public Health Quality Improvement Handbook* (Milwaukee, WI: Quality Press, 2009), pp.185–187.

# Appendix A

# The Matrix of Matrices

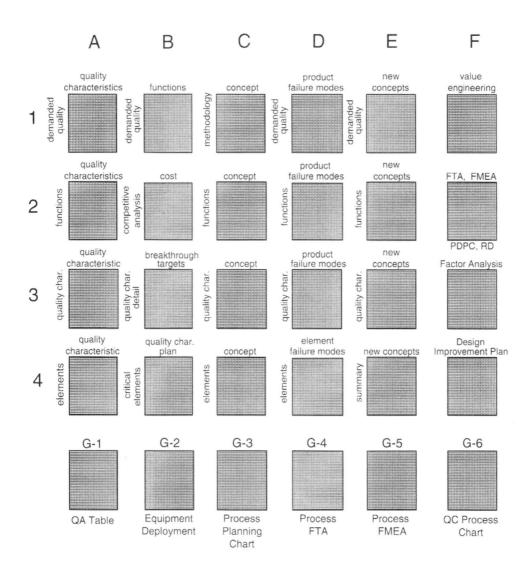

The Matrix of Matrices

From *Better Designs in Half the Time*, by Bob King, GOAL/QPC, © 1989.

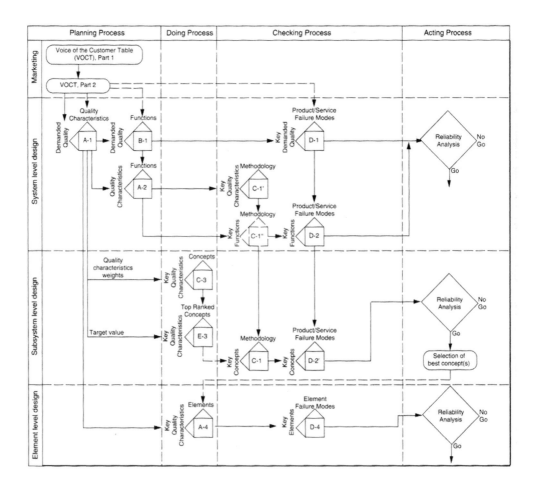

*Integration of All Four Design Flows*

# Appendix B

# QFD Software

QFD software is available from the following vendors to help you with the layout of the matrices and the calculation of weights. The authors suggest that the reader review all of the potential sources, and check for trial offers, technical support, and ease of use before deciding on a package:

- http://www.qfdcapture.com/

- http://www.sigmazone.com/qfdxl.htm

- http://www.qfdonline.com/qfd-builder-online-software

- http://www.isixsigma.com/tt/qfd/

- http://www.noweco.com/qfde.htm

- http://www.ideacore.com/

- http://www.mazur.net/qfd_software.htm

- http://www.qfdi.org/software.html

# Appendix C
## List of QFD Reference Books

The books listed below are available from:

- ASQ Quality Press

- Amazon

- QFD Institute Publications

- Productivity Press

***Quality Function Deployment: Integrating Customer Requirements into Product Design*** by Yoji Akao. ISBN 0915299410

***QFD: The Customer-Driven Approach to Quality Planning & Deployment*** by Shigeru Mizuno, Yoji Akao. ISBN 9283311221

***To Satisfy & Delight Your Customer: How to Manage for Customer Value*** by William Parde. ISBN 0932633358

***Measuring Customer Satisfaction: Development and Use of Questionnaires*** by Bob Hayes. ISBN 087389362X

***Quality Function Deployment: How to Make QFD Work For You*** by Louis Cohen. ISBN 0201633302

***Quality Up, Costs Down: A Quick and Easy Guide to QFD and Taguchi Methods*** by William Eureka and Nancy Ryan. ISBN 9780786302185

***Better Designs in Half the Time*** by Bob King, ISBN 1879364018

***The QFD Handbook*** by Jack B. Revelle, John W. Moran, and Charles Cox. ISBN 0471173819

*Quality Function Deployment: A Practitioner's Approach* by James L. Bossert. ISBN 0824783786

*Executive's Handbook on Quality Function Deployment: Defining Managements' Roles & Responsibilities* by Jack B. Revelle and John W. Moran. ISBN 0963822330

*Advanced QFD: Linking Technology to Market & Company Needs* by Larry M Shillito. ISBN: 0471033774

*Road Map to Repeatable Success: Using QFD to Implement Change* by Barbara A. Bicknell and Kris D. Bicknell. ISBN 9780849380198

*Step-By-Step QFD: Customer-Driven Product Design* by John Terninko. ISBN 1574441108

*Facilitating and Training in Quality Function Deployment* by S. Marsh, J.W. Moran, S. Nakui, and G. Hoffherr. ISBN 1879364182

# About the Authors

*Grace L. Duffy,* MBA, CLSSMBB, provides services in organizational and process improvement, leadership, quality, customer service, and teamwork. She designs and implements effective systems for business and management success. Her clients include government, healthcare, public health, education, manufacturing, services, and not-for-profit organizations. She is coauthor of *The Quality Improvement Handbook, The Executive Guide to Improvement and Change, Executive Focus: Your Life and Career*, and *The Public Health Quality Improvement Handbook.* Grace holds a master's degree in business administration from Georgia State University and a bachelor's degree in archaeology and anthropology from Brigham Young University. She is an ASQ certified manager of quality/organizational excellence, certified quality improvement associate, and certified quality auditor. Grace is a certified Lean-Six Sigma Master Black Belt and manager of process improvement. She is an ASQ fellow and past vice president of ASQ.

During her 20 years with IBM, Grace held a series of positions in technical design, services, management, and process improvement. She helped design and deliver IBM's executive quality training in the late 1980s. Grace retired from IBM in 1993 as head of corporate technical education. Grace served with Trident Technical College in Charleston, South Carolina, for 10 years as department head for business, curriculum owner, and instructor for Trident's Quality and Corporate Management programs and as a dean for management and performance consulting to private industry. Grace is a member of ASTD, ISPI, and ASQ. Grace can be reached at grace683@embarqmail.com.

*John W. Moran,* MBA, PhD, CMC, CQM, CQIA, is Senior Fellow in the Division of Health Policy and Management at the University of Minnesota, School of Public Health, and a senior quality advisor to the Public Health Foundation. He brings to PHF over 30 years of quality improvement expertise in developing quality improvement tools and training programs, implementing and evaluating quality improvement programs, and writing articles and books on quality improvement methods. Dr. Moran is a retired senior vice president of information systems, administrative and diagnostic services at New England Baptist Hospital.

He was previously chief operating officer of Changing Healthcare, Inc., specializing in management consulting and educational support to healthcare organizations. For 21 years, Dr. Moran was employed at Polaroid Corporation where he worked in various senior management capacities in manufacturing, engineering, and quality. His last position was as the director of Worldwide Quality and Systems.

Dr. Moran has authored numerous articles, case studies, and textbooks in healthcare, quality function deployment, and process redesign. His most recent books include *The Public Health Quality Improvement Handbook, Executive Focus: Focusing Your Life and Career, The Executive Guide to Improvement and Change, Action Strategies for Healthcare Leaders, The Quality Function Deployment Handbook, Management Development and Training, The Future Focused Organization, Breakthrough Thinking,* and *Growing Teams.*

Dr. Moran has been active in the American Society for Quality (ASQ) as a fellow of the society and serving as division chair, vice chair of technology, and chair of the ASQ Certification Committee, and a member of the Standing Review Board of Quality Press. Dr. Moran is an ASQ certified manager of quality/organizational excellence (CMQ/OE). He is a certified management consultant (CMC) by the Institute of Management Consultants. Dr. Moran is a 1993–2001 RIT/USA Today Quality Cup judge in healthcare and a member of the Malcolm Baldrige board of examiners. He was a founder and past member of the board of directors of the Massachusetts Quality Award. Dr. Moran earned BS, MBA, MS, and PhD degrees in Education from Walden University (1977). For 20 years Dr. Moran was an adjunct professor in the Graduate and Undergraduate School of Engineering at the University of Massachusetts at Lowell.

He may be reached at the Public Health Foundation at (202) 218-4423 and by e-mail at jmoran@phf.org.

**William Riley,** PhD, is associate dean, School of Public Heath, University of Minnesota. He specializes in the area of quality improvement and quality control and safety. He teaches healthcare quality improvement, finance, and process control. Dr. Riley has over 20 years of experience as a senior healthcare executive and has held the position of president and CEO of several healthcare organizations, including an integrated delivery system, a large multispecialty medical group, and a health plan joint venture. In these capacities, he has had extensive experience developing and implementing effective quality control systems, as well as leading numerous process improvement initiatives. He is the author of numerous studies and articles related to quality control, patient safety, and healthcare management. He has consulted nationally on numerous quality improvement projects. Dr. Riley is currently the principal investigator on a multiyear study leading an interdisciplinary team of physicians, nurses, and administrators to improve patient safety and develop innovative safety training programs.

# Index

5 Ss, 123—124

## A

A-1 matrix, 173, 176
Abusabha, F., 5n12
AC. *See* appraisal cost
Accreditation Coalition Quality Improvement
    Subgroup, 2
*Advanced QFD: Linking Technology to*
    *Market & Company Needs*, 188
Akao, Y., 20, 187
Anderson, D., 16n25
appraisal cost (AC), 77
assessment, 135–136

## B

Baldrige National Quality Improvement
    Program, 1n4
Barry, R., 62n3
batch size reduction, 125–126
Bauer, J., 131n2, 143n2, 155n10
Beecroft, G., 37n1, 131n1, 153n9
Beitsch, L., 2n6, 3n7, 156n11
Benbow, D. W., 61n2
Berger, C., 96n6
better, 106–107
*Better Designs in Half the Time*, 187
Bialek, R., 2n5, 2n6, 3n7, 13n22, 96n5, 119n1,
    119n2, 132n3, 150n6, 151n7, 161n14,
    161n16, 177n1
Bicknell, Barbara A., 188
Bicknell, Kris D., 188
big QI, 5–6, 13–15
Blitz, A., 24n7
Bossert, James L., 188

bottleneck, 54
bottom line, 70–77
Brubaker, C.E., 62n3
budget, 70–77
Burns, D., 16n25
business process focus, 107–108
Byrne, G., 24n7

## C

Carpenter, W. R., 148n5
Champy, J., 133n5
change management, 105–106
changeover, quick, 127
characteristics, measurement, 84–89
Chen, G., 5n12
client relationship model, 37–38
Cofsky, A., 2n6, 3n7
Cohen, Louis, 187
communication plan, establishing, 161–163
competitive benchmarking, 20
concept, 167
continuous quality improvement (CQI), 6
control issues, 156–159
COPQ. *See* cost of poor quality
COQ. *See* cost of quality
core activities, 31–32
core process, 54–55
core process redesign (CPR), 132
    model, 135–139, 140
    pathway, 135
    nature of, 55
Corso, L., 2n6, 3n7, 86n2
cost of poor quality (COPQ), 110–111
cost of quality, 77–78
    and leadership, 80
    contributions, 78–80

Cox, C., 13n23, 20n3, 20n4, 44n3, 44n4, 187
CPR. *See* core process redesign
CQI. *See* continuous quality improvement
cross-functional team, 145–146
current state value map, 59–60
customer
    demands, 174
    focus, 40
    needs, 46
    service, 38–47

**D**

data, for performance improvement, 89–90
decision making process, 153–155
decision making, as a team, 153
decisions, attributes, 155–156
Defeo, J., 117n8
Deming, W. E., 22, 96–97, 97n8, 107n7
design flaws, integration, 184
development processes, 31
diagram, solution and effect, 177
disconnect, 54
DMAIC, 24, 110–116, 121, 122
DMEDI, 24
Drucker, Peter, 67
Duffy, G., 2n5, 13n22, 37n1, 96n5, 105n5,
    105n6, 119n1, 119n2, 131n1, 131n2,
    131n3, 143n2, 145n4, 150n6, 151n7,
    153n9, 155n10, 156n11, 160n13, 161n14,
    161n16, 177n1

**E**

Edersheim, E. H., 67n2
Edmunds, L. S., 5n12
EFC. *See* external failure cost
effectiveness
    as a team, 150–153
    as a team member, 149–150
element, 167
empowerment, 149
Eureka, William, 187
Evans, J. R., 102n3
*Executive Guide to Improvement and Change,
    The*, 131
*Executive's Handbook on Quality Function
    Deployment: Defining Management's
    Roles and Responsibilities*, 188
external failure cost (EFC), 77
externally focused organization, vs. internally
    focused, 69–70

**F**

*Facilitating and Training in Quality Function
    Deployment*, 188
faster, 104–106
Feigenbaum, A. M., 77, 77n7
Fine, D., 33n2
flow, 127
focus, 135
Fried, B., 148n5
front-line staff, 148
Fukuhara, T., 20
function, 167
future state value map, 60–61

**G**

George, M. L., 13n24, 72n4, 101n1, 145n3
George, Michael, 101
Gibbs, L., 49n1
Goizueta, Roberto, 132
good decision, attributes, 155–156
Green, C. G., 5n13
Gryna, A. V., 77n8
Grzegorz, G., 30n1

**H**

Hammer, M., 133n5
Handler, A., 97n9
Hansen, M.A., 33n2
Harison, M., 5n13
Harrington, H.J., 77n6, 77n9
Hayes, Bob, 187
Henderson, K., 5n13
Henry, B., 105n6
Hoffher, G., 188
house, 174
House of Lean, 123
    building blocks, 123–128, 131–139
    foundation, 129
    roof, 130
    steps into, 129
House of Lean-Six Sigma
    techniques, 119–123
    tools, 119–123
houses of quality, 150, 168, 169

**I**

IFC. *See* internal failure cost
immunization map, 75–75

implementation, 138–139
    time frame, 160–163
    time line, 162
improvement ideas, 148
improvement team, 145
indicators, performance, 91
individual level quality improvement, 2, 13–15, 33–36
individual qi, 13–15, 33–36
inefficiencies, identifying, 54
influence issues, 156–159
inspection, 54
integrated processes, 29–33
integrated quality improvement, 27–36
internal failure cost (IFC), 77
internally focused organization, vs. externally focused, 69–70
Ishikawa, K., 102, 102n2
Issel, M., 97n9

**J**

Jing-hua Shi, Q. S., 77n10
JIT. *See* just-in-time
Johnson, S. B., 19n2
Joiner, B. L., 143n1, 161n15
Juran, J. M., 77, 77n5
Juran, Joseph A., 22
just-in-time (JIT), 101

**K**

kanban, 101
kano model, 44–45
King, Bob, 187
Kubiak, T. M., 61n2

**L**

Langley, G. J., 3n8, 8n21
leadership involvement, 107
leadership visibility, 107
lean and six sigma, combining, 109
lean tools, 28
Lean-Six Sigma, 13, 22–25, 49–50, 101–104
    and quality function deployment, 22, 27–36
    evolution, 103
    roles, 112–113
lean, defined, 23
Lee, S., 16n25
Lenihan, A., 5n13

Lindsay, W. M., 102n3
little qi, 3–6, 13–15
Lubowe, D., 24n7

**M**

macro level quality improvement, 2, 5–6, 13–15, 27–36
MAPP. *See* mobilizing for action through planning and partnerships
Marsh, S., 188
master black belt, 110
matrices matrix, 183
matrix
    A-1, 173, 176
    L-shaped, 166
    MxN, 166
    navigating, 173–182
Maxey, J., 72n4
MBB. *See* master black belt
McCullough, Mac, 49
McKoy, K., 4n11, 6n15, 16n25
measurement characteristics, 84–89
measures
    developing, 159–160
    final reporting, 83–84
    interim reporting, 83–84
    performance, 90, 92, 95
*Measuring Customer Satisfaction: Development and Use of Questionnaires*, 187
meso level quality improvement, 7, 15, 27–36
meso-level activities, process measures, 98–99
micro level quality improvement, 2, 3–5, 27–36
micro-level activities, process measures, 98–99
milestones
    final reporting, 83–84
    interim reporting, 83–84
Minnesota Health Alert Network, 9–13
Minnesota Public Health Collaboration for Quality Improvement (MPHCQI), 3, 7–13, 15–17
Minnesota Women, Infants, and Children (WIC), 4
Mizuno, Shigero, 187
MLC. *See* multi-state learning collaborative
Mobilizing for Action through Planning and Partnerships (MAPP), 1, 1n2, 38, 67n1
Moran, J., 2n5, 2n6, 19n1, 20n3, 20n4, 20n5, 37n1, 44n3, 44n4, 96n5, 119n1, 119n2, 132n3, 145n4, 150n6, 151n7, 155n10, 156n11, 161n14, 161n16, 177n1
Moran, J. W., 3n7, 13n22, 13n23, 105n5, 105n6, 131n1, 153n9, 187, 188

MPHCQI. *See* Minnesota Public Health Collaboration for Quality Improvement
Multi-State Learning Collaborative (MLC), 8

**N**

Nakui, S., 188
natural team, 144–145
negotiation, 136
Nolan, K. M., 3n8, 8n21
Nolan, T. W., 3n8, 8n21
non-value added, 56
Norman, C. L., 3n8, 8n21
norming, 158

**O**

OCHD. *See* Orange County Health (FL) Department (OCHD)
opportunity map, 56–57
optimize, 49
Orange County Health (FL) Department (OCHD), 72
organization
    externally focused vs. internally focused, 69–70
    internally focused vs. externally focused, 69–70
organizational redesign, areas of, 133–134
Osborne, D., 39n2

**P**

Parde, William, 187
Parsons, H., 3n9, 6n14, 16n25, 105n6
patient flow, visualizing, 57–58
PC. *See* Prevention cost
PDCA. *See* plan-do-check-act (PDCA)
PDSA. *See* plan-do-check-act (PDCA)
Pennsylvania Department of Health, 96
performance improvement, using data, 89–90
performance indicators, 91
performance management, 89–90
    cycle, 96–98
    definitions, 90–91
    system, 94–95
performance measures, 89, 90, 92, 95
performance standards, 89, 90
    examples, 91
performance targets, 91, 94
PERT. *See* program evaluation and review technique
plan-do-check-act, 3, 102, 104–106, 119–120
plan-do-check-act cycle, 120

plan-do-study-act (PDSA). *See* plan-do-check-act (PDCA)
Planning and Performance Measurement Reporting System (PPMRS), 7
PPMRS. *See* Planning and Performance Measurement Reporting System
prevention cost (PC), 77
Price, M., 72n4
problem statement, 158
process, 55
    analyzing, 50–54
    decision making, 153–155
    features, 54–55
    structure, 50
process analysis, 49–65
process boundaries, 51
process costing summary, 76
process flow comparisons, 24
process improvement, 3
    maintaining, 159–160
process lead time, 55
process map, 50
    creating, 51–54
    inefficiencies, 54
    opportunity map, 56–57
    symbols, 52, 57
    types of, 55–61
process measures
    meso-level activities, 98–99
    micro-level activities, 98–99
process problem, visualizing, 148
program evaluation and review technique (PERT), 121
progress reporting, 92–94, 95–96
project management, 104–109
project team, 146
Provost, L. P., 3n8, 8n21
Pruzek, R., 5n12
Public Health Foundation, 96
*Public Health Quality Improvement Handbook, The*, 119, 132
pull, 127
Pyzdek, T., 153n8

**Q**

*The QFD Handbook*, 187
QFD. *See* quality function deployment
*QFD: The Customer-Driven Approach to Quality Planning & Deployment*, 187
quality characteristics, 167
quality function deployment (QFD), 13, 19–22
    Lean-Six Sigma, 22, 27–36
    matrices, 173–182

reference books, 187–188
software, 185
voice of the customer, 80–81
quality function deployment study, conducting, 165–171
quality function deployment team
developing, 143–144
types, 144–146
*Quality Function Deployment: A Practitioner's Approach*, 188
*Quality Function Deployment: How to Make QFD Work For You*, 187
*Quality Function Deployment: Integrating Customer Requirements into Product Design*, 187
quality improvement, 89
large scale, 6–13
process, 94
system level, 6–13
*Quality Up, Costs Down: A Quick and Easy Guide to QFD and Taguchi Methods*, 187
quality, at source, 126

**R**

Ramo Wooldridge Corporation, 19
rapid cycle change, 104–109
red zone, 139
redesign, 137–138
redundancy, 54
relationships, 167
repetition, 105
reporting progress, 89, 95–96
requirements interface matrix (RIM), 19, 20n3, 20n4, 20n5, 44n3, 44n4
ReVelle, J. B., 13n23, 187, 188
rework, 54
Riley, W., 2n6, 3n7, 3n9, 4n11, 6n14, 6n15, 16n25, 105n5, 105n6, 145n4
RIM. *See* requirements interface matrix
*Road Map to Repeatable Success: Using QFD to Implement Change*, 188
Robert Wood Johnson Foundation, 8
Roggenhoffer, S., 33n2
Rowlands, D. P., 72n4
Russo, P., 2n6
Ryan, Nancy, 187

**S**

Saginaw County, MI, 95–96
Sainfort, F., 16n25
saturation, 105
Scholites, P. R., 143n1, 161n15

self-directed team, 146
Shea, T., 49n1
Sheng-jie, L., 77n10
Shillito, Larry M., 188
simplify, 49
six sigma and lean, combining, 109
six sigma tools, 28
smarter, 107–109
Smith, A. C., 62n3
solution and effect diagram, 177
source quality, 126
spaghetti diagram, 61–62, 63
standardized layout, 125
standards, performance, 90, 91
*Step-by-Step QFD: Customer-Driven Product Design*, 188
storage, 127
strategic management, 67
processes, 31
Stratton, H., 5n12
streamline, 49
streamlined layout, 125
Streibel, B. J., 143n1, 161n15
support, 148
processes, 33, 54–55
symbols, process map, 52, 57
system, 55
system creation, using integrated processes, 29–33
system level quality improvement, 6–13
system-level, 168
systemwide integration, 106–107

**T**

targets, performance, 91, 94
team effectiveness, 156–159
team, 126
cross-functional, 145–146
decision making, 153
effective, 150–153
effective members, 149–150
improvement, 145
natural, 144–145
project, 146
self-directed, 146
types, 144–146
value, 147–149
technical characteristics tree diagram, 178
Terninko, John, 188
Thingstad-Boe, D., 3n9, 6n14
time chart, vs. value-added, 62–64
time frame, implementing, 160–163

*To Satisfy & Delight Your Customer: How to Manage for Customer Value*, 187
total productive maintenance, 127
total quality management (TQM), 101–102
Toyota production system (TPS), 101
TPS. *See* Toyota production system
TQM. *See* total quality management
transitional time line, 139
tree diagram, 167
    technical characteristics, 178
    voice of the customer, 175
Tregear, R., 99n10
Turnock, B., 97n9

## U

University of Michigan, 95–96
University of Minnesota School of Public Health, 8, 49

## V

value added, 56
value map
    current state, 59–60
    future state, 60–61

value stream mapping (VSM), 57, 62–64, 128
value-added, vs. time chart, 62–64
virtual team, 146
visual controls, 124–125
VOC. *See* voice of the customer
voice of the customer (VOC), 20, 27, 35, 42–43, 45, 108–109
    tree diagram, 175
voice of the process, 152
VSM. *See* value stream mapping

## W

waste reduction, 49–65
waste, types of, 64, 65
Westcott, R. T., 131n2, 143n2
*What Is Total Quality Control?*, 102
WIC. *See* Minnesota Women, Infants, and Children
Wiesner, P. J., 86n2
Woelfel, M. L., 5n12
Wood, D. C., 80n11

## Z

Zitzer, P., 96n6

# Belong to the Quality Community!

Established in 1946, ASQ is a global community of quality experts in all fields and industries. ASQ is dedicated to the promotion and advancement of quality tools, principles, and practices in the workplace and in the community.

The Society also serves as an advocate for quality. Its members have informed and advised the U.S. Congress, government agencies, state legislatures, and other groups and individuals worldwide on quality-related topics.

## Vision

By making quality a global priority, an organizational imperative, and a personal ethic, ASQ becomes the community of choice for everyone who seeks quality technology, concepts, or tools to improve themselves and their world.

## ASQ is...

- More than 90,000 individuals and 700 companies in more than 100 countries

- The world's largest organization dedicated to promoting quality

- A community of professionals striving to bring quality to their work and their lives

- The administrator of the Malcolm Baldrige National Quality Award

- A supporter of quality in all sectors including manufacturing, service, healthcare, government, and education

- YOU

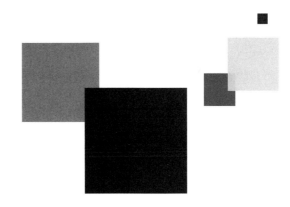

**Visit www.asq.org for more information.**

ASQ

# ASQ Membership

Research shows that people who join associations experience increased job satisfaction, earn more, and are generally happier*. ASQ membership can help you achieve this while providing the tools you need to be successful in your industry and to distinguish yourself from your competition. So why wouldn't you want to be a part of ASQ?

## Networking

Have the opportunity to meet, communicate, and collaborate with your peers within the quality community through conferences and local ASQ section meetings, ASQ forums or divisions, ASQ Communities of Quality discussion boards, and more.

## Professional Development

Access a wide variety of professional development tools such as books, training, and certifications at a discounted price. Also, ASQ certifications and the ASQ Career Center help enhance your quality knowledge and take your career to the next level.

## Solutions

Find answers to all your quality problems, big and small, with ASQ's Knowledge Center, mentoring program, various e-newsletters, *Quality Progress* magazine, and industry-specific products.

## Access to Information

Learn classic and current quality principles and theories in ASQ's Quality Information Center (QIC), *ASQ Weekly* e-newsletter, and product offerings.

## Advocacy Programs

ASQ helps create a better community, government, and world through initiatives that include social responsibility, Washington advocacy, and Community Good Works.

**Visit www.asq.org/membership for more information on ASQ membership.**

*2008, The William E. Smith Institute for Association Research

# ASQ Certification

ASQ certification is formal recognition by ASQ that an individual has demonstrated a proficiency within, and comprehension of, a specified body of knowledge at a point in time. Nearly 150,000 certifications have been issued. ASQ has members in more than 100 countries, in all industries, and in all cultures. ASQ certification is internationally accepted and recognized.

## Benefits to the Individual

- New skills gained and proficiency upgraded
- Investment in your career
- Mark of technical excellence
- Assurance that you are current with emerging technologies
- Discriminator in the marketplace
- Certified professionals earn more than their uncertified counterparts
- Certification is endorsed by more than 125 companies

## Benefits to the Organization

- Investment in the company's future
- Certified individuals can perfect and share new techniques in the workplace
- Certified staff are knowledgeable and able to assure product and service quality

Quality is a global concept. It spans borders, cultures, and languages. No matter what country your customers live in or what language they speak, they demand quality products and services. You and your organization also benefit from quality tools and practices. Acquire the knowledge to position yourself and your organization ahead of your competition.

**Certifications Include**

- Biomedical Auditor – CBA
- Calibration Technician – CCT
- HACCP Auditor – CHA
- Pharmaceutical GMP Professional – CPGP
- Quality Inspector – CQI
- Quality Auditor – CQA
- Quality Engineer – CQE
- Quality Improvement Associate – CQIA
- Quality Technician – CQT
- Quality Process Analyst – CQPA
- Reliability Engineer – CRE
- Six Sigma Black Belt – CSSBB
- Six Sigma Green Belt – CSSGB
- Software Quality Engineer – CSQE
- Manager of Quality/Organizational Excellence – CMQ/OE

**Visit www.asq.org/certification to apply today!**

# ASQ Training

## Classroom-based Training

ASQ offers training in a traditional classroom setting on a variety of topics. Our instructors are quality experts and lead courses that range from one day to four weeks, in several different cities. Classroom-based training is designed to improve quality and your organization's bottom line. Benefit from quality experts; from comprehensive, cutting-edge information; and from peers eager to share their experiences.

## Web-based Training

### Virtual Courses

ASQ's virtual courses provide the same expert instructors, course materials, interaction with other students, and ability to earn CEUs and RUs as our classroom-based training, without the hassle and expenses of travel. Learn in the comfort of your own home or workplace. All you need is a computer with Internet access and a telephone.

## Self-paced Online Programs

These online programs allow you to work at your own pace while obtaining the quality knowledge you need. Access them whenever it is convenient for you, accommodating your schedule.

### Some Training Topics Include

- Auditing
- Basic Quality
- Engineering
- Education
- Healthcare
- Government
- Food Safety
- ISO
- Leadership
- Lean
- Quality Management
- Reliability
- Six Sigma
- Social Responsibility

**Visit www.asq.org/training for more information.**